# SCIENCE AND THE NATION

# SCIENCE AND THE NATION
Essays by Cambridge Graduates with an Introduction by the Right Hon. Lord Moulton, K.C.B., F.R.S.

EDITED BY

A. C. SEWARD, F.R.S.
Master of Downing College, Cambridge

*Essay Index Reprint Series*

BOOKS FOR LIBRARIES PRESS, INC.
FREEPORT, NEW YORK

First published 1917
Reprinted 1967

"What people call Applied Science is nothing but the application of Pure Science to particular classes of problems."

T. H. HUXLEY

LIBRARY OF CONGRESS CATALOG CARD NUMBER:
67-26780
PRINTED IN THE UNITED STATES OF AMERICA

# PREFACE

DURING the last two years there has been an increasing tendency to realize the pressing urgency not only for extending and improving scientific teaching but for a whole-hearted recognition, both by the individual and the State, of the supreme importance of utilizing and developing in the fullest measure the aptitude for scientific research which is unquestionably a characteristic of the British race. The time seemed propitious for emphasizing a particular aspect of the general question of the interdependence of many phases of national prosperity and a just appreciation of the value of pure science. "Original research," as the late Prof. Meldola said, "is in itself the most powerful weapon that has been or ever can be wielded by mankind in struggling with the great problems which nature offers on all sides for solution."

It is widely believed that technical education stands for efficiency and prosperity, but pure science is regarded as something apart—a purely academic subject. It was with a view to demonstrate the fallacy of this distinction that the present volume was suggested. 'Science and the Nation' might be taken as a text for many discourses on the place of science in school curricula, on the necessity for affording every boy an opportunity of learning something of natural phenomena, and on the supreme importance of a sympathetic and intelligent attitude towards the natural sciences on the part of those entrusted with the direction of national affairs. While all these questions receive some attention in the following essays, the primary object of the authors is the presentation of facts and arguments which may enable the reader to grasp in its true perspective the relation of pure science to applied science, "the worker in pure science discovers; his fellow in applied science utilizes." It is often impossible to prophesy whether or not a particular branch of natural knowledge will have a bearing upon industrial or technical problems. An analysis of many striking achievements into the successive stages of their development often discloses some discovery which pointed the way to results of the greatest value. The history of scientific discovery furnishes numerous illustrations of the far reaching importance of pure science as the force which gave the impulse to developments that have led to industrial prosperity or to the betterment of the race.

  Schemes of reform and reconstruction formulated under the present abnormal conditions are apt to be hastily conceived and ill-proportioned. To be successful they must be based on the firm foundation of experience: it is the aim of the authors of

## PREFACE

the essays, whose willingness to accede to the editor's request for contributions calls for a word of cordial acknowledgment, to present the results of experience in scientific investigation, to illustrate by concrete examples the sources of progress in a few departments of knowledge and so make clear to the layman the position of research as a factor in national prosperity.

It is an especial pleasure to thank Lord Moulton for contributing an Introduction.

A. C. SEWARD

DOWNING COLLEGE LODGE
*January* 5, 1917

# INTRODUCTION

By The Right Hon. LORD MOULTON, K.C.B., F.R.S.

The professed object of the compilation of this book of essays is the assertion of the importance of what is usually known as "Pure Science." It admits that it is motivated by a fear lest the universal feeling that England has been remiss in the cultivation of large branches of Industrial Science in the past and the wide-spread determination to remedy this in the future may lead to a neglect—absolute or comparative—of Pure Science after the War is over and that the pursuit of Pure Science may suffer by reason of the concentration of national effort in the direction of the more utilitarian applications of Scientific Research.

The immediate outcome of this apprehension has been the admirable collection of Essays to which I have been asked to write this Introduction. I feel greatly honoured by being selected for the task. Each one of these Essays has been written by some one who, by lifelong study and practice of the Branch of Science to which it relates, has qualified himself to give a just and authoritative description of the work that has already been done

## INTRODUCTION

as well as of the bearing of that work on the present and its promise for the future. The recital of the results obtained is so framed that it not only makes clear to any intelligent reader the achievements of Science but it reveals them as the result of growth due to the steady pursuit of knowledge by rational and intelligent research. In this way these achievements, however great and however startling in themselves and however far-reaching in their consequences, are shewn to be only a first crop from a still fertile ground, which will shew a like fruitfulness in the future if its cultivation be not neglected. The value of Essays such as these, dealing broadly speaking with the whole Realm of Science, is at the present moment difficult to overestimate. They will prove invaluable to those who seek to broaden the interest of our Nation in Scientific Research.

But I do not share the fear that so-called Pure Science is in danger of being neglected in the revival of industrial effort to which we all look forward. The distinction between Pure Science and Applied Science is vague and artificial and, so far as my observation goes, it does not exist as a guiding principle in the minds of those classes to whom we must look for the force which will place Science in its right position in England. It is a distinction which is more actively present to the minds of those who are engaged in abstruse research than to the mind of the general public.

# INTRODUCTION

They are conscious that their work deals with matters so abstruse as to be fully understood by those only who have themselves studied the subject and hence they conceive that members of the general public can feel no interest in it. But this is not so. From time to time so many marvels have been suddenly sprung upon us in the past which have owed their birth to research carried on in silence in laboratories and the like that the general public is quite ready to treat such homes of research as mysterious workshops, the methods and aims of which are beyond them but from which great discoveries may at any moment arise. It looks forward with hope to these future discoveries and it feels too much in awe of the secrets of Science to desire to control or criticise the methods by which they are arrived at.

The word "research" has of late years been used too frequently as little more than a cant phrase dear to educationalists but carrying with it no clear or definite meaning, and if there is any patent or latent hostility to research it is mainly due to the way in which the word has thus been treated by its self-styled champions. But (as I am glad to say is frequently the case even in the arena of legal conflicts) the blunders of the advocate have not been sufficient to hide the merits of his case. Not only thoughtful educated men but even the members of the general public are beginning to realise that it is to research in

# INTRODUCTION

its proper signification that we owe the knowledge of the wealth of the world in which we are placed —of the power that is within our grasp. The man engaged on research is like the mining prospector who may discover that rocks which seem to the ordinary eye indistinguishable from the barren masses that surround them are in reality teeming with riches. But for research one would never have known that the coal-tar oils which resemble so closely in their general characteristics the Paraffins or Petroleums are capable of entering into combinations of such novelty and complexity that they now furnish the whole world with dyes and chemical products of priceless value. It is the application of research to the problems of metallurgy that has caused the additions to our knowledge of metals during the last 50 years to be greater than all that had been learnt in the ages that had elapsed since man first began to work metals. And what is the most remarkable of all, we find that through the introduction of research the empirical handling of the problems of organic life is being step by step replaced by an assured treatment based on a conscious and realised connection between cause and effect. All these changes are due to Research. Scientific research has removed our previous ignorance of the properties and powers of the things around us and has taught us what they are and how they can be used. It is not too strong a simile to say that without the teaching of Science man blunders through life much as a card player would blunder through a game of cards if he did not take the trouble to look at the cards in his hand and learn their value.

I do not underestimate the value of the traditional knowledge that we have inherited from our ancestors. The long ages that preceded the dawn of experimental science gave scope for advance by the slow process of unaided observation and for the half-unconscious education which results from mere experience. Moreover in these ages there have appeared from time to time men who have in a rude and unsystematical way carried out true experimental research. But we can no longer wait for the slow results of casual discovery. The aim of those who would encourage research is to advance our knowledge of the world around us by the only way in which swift and assured progress can be made, namely by experimental investigation in the hands of men who are concentrating their attention on the problems on which they are engaged. By the use of these means we may confidently count upon success. The world around us teems with mysteries. There is scarcely one section of it which does not lead to bewilderment when an attempt is made to probe it to the depths. But there is one clue given to us which enables us to thread the maze. However multitudinous, however varied, however confusing in their interaction the laws of Nature may be, we have the firm belief that they are immutable. On this single base rests the whole of Science. The answer that is wrung from Nature by an experiment to-day holds good for all time. The numberless errors into which scientific men have fallen and into which for a time they may have led the scientific beliefs of their generation are due to their misunderstanding the answer which Nature has given, and these errors are inevitably corrected by others who have put the question more skilfully or have more accurately read the answer. The replies that she gives to our questions are always truthful and will therefore in due time be recognised as consistent.

These laws of Nature are but another name for that which I have already referred to as the wealth of the world in which we live. The properties of every element and of every combination of elements are just as much included in this totality of the laws of Nature as is the law of gravitation. This our prison-house is furnished with collections and combinations of substances governed by immutable laws which they obey under whatever circumstances we call upon them to do so. The knowledge of these immutable laws—these properties of substances—is the whole of our wealth and it is the conscious or unconscious utilisation of them which constitutes all the achievements of mankind.

The main charm of this collection of Essays is the presentation of the manner in which this investigation of the furniture of the world has already

## INTRODUCTION

affected practical life in the various and widely distinct branches of human effort.

In such a presentation it was inevitable that Chemistry should take the first place. Its growth during the last half century has been startlingly rapid in Pure Science, but even this is dwarfed by its achievements in Industrial Life where in the shape of dyes, pharmaceutical and photographic products it has forced itself upon the attention of every member of the community. The claims of Physics secure for it a right to the second place. Considered as a whole it has done more to mould industrial life than any other department of Science. But its triumphs came earlier than those of Chemistry and the progress of Physical Science during the last 50 years would not strike the ordinary observer with any comparatively equal effect were it not that electricity in the shape of telegraphy, electric light and engineering has changed the whole possibilities of human existence within that time. Those who doubt this had better try to picture to themselves what would have been the course of the present War had electricity in the shape of telegraphy and engineering not existed.

It is not my intention to refer specifically to the individual Essays contained in this volume but I have derived special pleasure from the group that deals with organic life in health and disease. This constitutes the most recently captured domain of

# INTRODUCTION

Experimental Research, and it is also that which is least known to the public. Till a comparatively recent date even students of Science would have been prepared to concede that the mysteries of life and above all the mysteries of descent must be left to experience and observation and that the experimental method could not hope to arrive at accurate and reliable rules of action such as those obtainable in the inorganic world. But such work as that described by Professor Biffen and his collaborators tell a very different tale. Thanks largely to the Pure Science of Mendel we are rapidly acquiring the power of reorganising the existing vegetable kingdom so as to make new varieties of useful plants which will be secure from attacks from their enemies and will yield a larger return to the cultivator.

On the other hand Experimental Science is giving to us clear ideas on the effect of foods both as to health and growth. We are learning what is the specific effect of various forms of nutrition and at the same time we are being taught the dangers that may arise from the absence of certain essentials in food, the very existence of which was hitherto unsuspected. It will be interesting to see how rapidly the teachings of this branch of research will be accepted by the class to which they are of the most importance, namely, our Agriculturists. Agriculture is probably the oldest art in the world and it has hitherto reposed mainly on experience and tradition. The day is approaching when this must be changed and the teaching of Experimental Science must be listened to even in Agriculture if we are to bear the burden of supporting the enormous and ever-growing populations of to-day. Personally I have little doubt of success in this direction. Improved methods will here have less to fear from that which, especially in England, is their most formidable enemy in the industrial world, namely the inertia of capital. It requires no elaborate plant to enable the farmer to use a pure pedigree wheat in his fields and to guide his choice of manures by sound principles. That he is naturally conservative in his methods is a necessity of his art but when better methods are brought to his knowledge which are supported by practical demonstrations such as those set out in these Essays the force of which, he, of all men, is best capable of appreciating I have little fear that he will not shew himself willing to learn.

I have more doubt of the prompt acceptance of the new teaching as to Disease. Medical Practice has for so many ages rested on empiricism and tradition and has been so completely dominated by authority that it is hard for it to give a speedy welcome to new knowledge. Fortunately the invasion has already been so successful that so far as Causes are concerned the victory is gained. No one refuses to accept the existence and effects of Pathogenic Bacteria or Protozoa. But there is and must for a long time be a wide difference of opinion as to the effect which the new knowledge ought to have upon the treatment of disease. The Essays which deal with these subjects set out in clear light the instances where success has been obtained in this respect and they constitute an unchallengeable argument in favour of Pure Science or as I should prefer to call it Experimental Research motivated purely by the desire to increase knowledge. The more intricate the subject-matter the more necessary it is that those engaged in the research should be free to investigate the whole field fully and exhaustively. The game has to be stalked from long distances and often by circuitous routes. It is no longer possible to walk directly up to it.

Passing from these more obvious examples of Experimental Research one comes to the Essay on the progress of Metallurgy. From this there will be few, except those who are specialists in the question, who will not be surprised as well as delighted by the account of the past growth and the promise of future growth of scientific knowledge in a subject which one would have thought was specially the domain of the empiricists. Handled as it is, in these Essays, it furnishes in abundance the rich intellectual pleasure of surprise that does not owe its charm to wonder—that agreeable product of conscious ignorance.

The publication of this collection of Essays has, as I have said, been prompted by the fear lest in the eagerness to extend the application of scientific knowledge to Industrial developments after the War there should be a tendency even in the centres of education to cultivate the practical side alone. But it will have a still more important effect. It will I hope help to bring about the very industrial revolution the effect of which it fears. It is too lightly assumed that the English people will have learnt the lesson which the experiences of this War time ought to have taught them, namely that they must change their ways in very many departments of national industry. In the past they have contented themselves either with adhering to antiquated methods which ought long ago to have been superseded or with availing themselves of the new knowledge by permitting others to apply it for them. In the textile industries for example they were not only willing that their dyes should be manufactured abroad by methods which they did not attempt to master but also that even the use of these dyes should be taught to their dyers by the producers without any attempt to make them understand the rationale of the methods employed. The consequence of this has been a state of industrial dependence from which our industries cannot rescue themselves without deliberate and sustained effort on the part of both the employers and the employed.

That this will be made one hopes, but it can only be successful if we change radically our

## INTRODUCTION xix

conceptions of national education. It has been fashionable for the well-to-do to choose for their children an education devoid of Science and indeed devoid of continuous intellectual effort. So long as the subjects of education were mainly ancient languages and the humanities the knowledge which they thus failed to acquire was no great loss. Though the discipline of study would have been valuable the knowledge would have possessed no practical value except so far as it enabled them to earn a living by continuing the traditional system of education. But the fatal consequence of these educational methods was that it was considered no shame that a man should leave his University not only ignorant of Modern Languages and Science but also unprovided with any economical or commercial training that could be of value to him in practical life. This example has been followed by other classes of the community who have naturally accepted the standards of education adopted by the wealthier classes as being the best, and thus much of the best human material that England produces has been sent to its work in life without any special preparation for the task before it.

To remedy this in our Industries it is not sufficient that our youth should be taught the facts of Science. They must also be trained in its methods. In every industry there is scope for research and on it must depend the maintenance of our position

## INTRODUCTION

in the industrial struggle for existence. The methods of Research in Industrial and Pure Science do not differ in essence. The distinction lies in the nature and circumstances of the problems with which they deal. Hence there is no training so valuable for industrial life as that of being brought into close contact with those who are engaged in Scientific Research whether it be in University Laboratories or elsewhere.

By concentrating this work at our Universities and making the students see and take part in it we shall send out into the world a class of men fitted for carrying out the industrial research necessary for the maintenance of our position in trade. The tone of these Essays and the record they contain of the work that is being carried on at our English Universities shew that they at least are doing their share in training students in research and thus fitting them for a higher standard of practical work, and if the people of England are ready and willing to avail themselves of the educational opportunities thus given there need be no fear that in the years to come we shall be distanced by our foreign competitors.

# CONTENTS

| | PAGE |
|---|---|
| INTRODUCTION . . . . . . | viii |

 The Right Hon. LORD MOULTON, K.C.B., F.R.S.

THE NATIONAL IMPORTANCE OF CHEMISTRY .   1

 W. J. POPE, F.R.S., Professor of Chemistry in the University of Cambridge.

PHYSICAL RESEARCH AND THE WAY OF ITS APPLICATION . . . . .   24

 W. H. BRAGG, F.R.S., Quain Professor of Physics in the University of London.

THE MODERN SCIENCE OF METALS, PURE AND APPLIED . . . . . .   49

 W. ROSENHAIN, F.R.S., Superintendent of the Department of Metallurgy and Metallurgical Chemistry in the National Physical Laboratory.

MATHEMATICS IN RELATION TO PURE AND APPLIED SCIENCE . . . .   78

 E. W. HOBSON, F.R.S., Sadleirian Professor of Pure Mathematics in the University of Cambridge.

THE SCIENCE OF BOTANY AND THE ART OF INTENSIVE CULTIVATION . . .   106

 F. W. KEEBLE, F.R.S., Director of the Royal Horticultural Society's Gardens, Wisley.

# CONTENTS

| | PAGE |
|---|---|
| SCIENCE IN FORESTRY | 129 |

W. Dawson, M.A., Reader in Forestry in the University of Cambridge.

SYSTEMATIZED PLANT BREEDING . . . 146

R. H. Biffen, F.R.S., Professor of Agricultural Botany in the University of Cambridge.

AN AGRICULTURAL WAR PROBLEM . . 176

T. B. Wood, M.A., Drapers Professor of Agriculture in the University of Cambridge.

GEOLOGY AS AN ECONOMIC SCIENCE . . 205

Herbert H. Thomas, Sc.D., Secretary of the Geological Society of London.

MEDICINE AND EXPERIMENTAL SCIENCE . 228

F. Gowland Hopkins, F.R.S., Professor of Biochemistry in the University of Cambridge.

THE "SPECIFIC TREATMENT" OF DISEASE . 256

G. H. F. Nuttall, F.R.S., Quick Professor of Biology in the University of Cambridge.

FLIES AND DISEASE . . . . . 279

G. S. Graham-Smith, M.D., University Lecturer in Hygiene in the University of Cambridge.

THE GOVERNMENT OF SUBJECT PEOPLES 302

W. H. R. Rivers, F.R.S., Fellow of St John's College, Cambridge.

# THE NATIONAL IMPORTANCE OF CHEMISTRY

By W. J. Pope, F.R.S.

*Professor of Chemistry in the University of Cambridge.*

Any attempt to describe the manner in which modern Chemistry bears upon modern civilisation is complicated by the intimate relationship which exists between the purely abstract aspects of this science and its technical or practical applications. Each fresh addition to chemical science can be immediately fitted into its appropriate position in the great general scheme of Natural Philosophy; it cannot be placed with similar certainty in relation to the world at large because of the impossibility of foreseeing whether any new discovery, apparently of purely academic significance, may not unexpectedly assume high importance in connexion with the solution of some very practical problem.

Many illustrations might be given of the operation of this principle during quite recent times. Thus, half a century ago Organic Chemistry had made such progress as to suggest to its leaders the possibility of producing indigo artificially;

the suggestion proved a fruitful one and by a chain of events, which constitute a marvellous achievement of theoretical reasoning and of practical skill, indigo was produced from coal tar products. The technological possibilities of the synthetic indigo problem were, however, studied simultaneously with its purely scientific aspects and consequently artificial indigo is now manufactured at so low a cost that the production of the colouring matter from the plant has almost ceased. It is true that the manufacture of natural indigo, up to the present day, is carried out by methods which the Pharaohs might have criticised as conservative; it is also fairly certain that a comparatively small sum of money devoted to improving the culture of the indigo plant would so reduce the cost of natural indigo as to ruin the artificial manufacture. These obvious facts have not been acted upon, and consequently we find that in 1913 the German works manufactured artificial indigo to the value of about £2,000,000 and the producing companies paid annual dividends up to 30 per cent.

Whilst scientific and technical progress in Chemistry are intimately connected, and react so rapidly one upon the other that the two cannot be kept apart in any comprehensive discussion, it must also be remarked that all the different branches of chemical science and technology are interdependent to an extraordinary degree. The unhappy events of the last two years have given rise to a widespread belief that the science of Chemistry is largely responsible for the accentuation of the horrors associated with war. This belief is a mistaken one and arises from a failure to comprehend the part played by Chemistry in developing the resources and promoting the prosperity of any great modern nation. A flourishing chemical industry is a perpetual source of wealth to a country and the prime fount of countless ameliorations of the conditions of life—ameliorations which cannot be permanently confined to the nation from which they spring. But, in accordance with a natural law, so potent an agent for good becomes a powerful weapon in war, and the unfair use of the weapon cannot be charged against the specialist who devised the tool for some peaceful purpose. Signs are, indeed, not wanting which indicate that science has little to do with the control of German policy and methods. It is impossible to believe, for instance, that any scientific man ever suggested that the Flammenwerfer could possess any efficiency as a military weapon; it is, however, easy to visualise the chemical engineer producing such an archaic implement at the bidding of a non-scientific chief. German primary and secondary education is more intensely classical and literary than is British; its products naturally tend towards such an inherently false and proportionless outlook on life, affairs, and things as has been repeatedly exhibited to us by an unscrupulous enemy during the past two years.

The discussion of the bearing of Chemistry on national prosperity leads immediately to a consideration of the ramifications of the chemical industries and later to an examination of the way in which industrial chemical development must be secured by both academic and technical research work. So vast is the subject that for the present purpose some limitation of ambit must be premised; it will be convenient to omit the great metallurgical industries, the pottery and earthenware industries and others, which are indeed purely chemical but lend themselves appropriately to separate treatment, and to deal mainly with those industries which produce more or less pure chemical compounds. Such chemical compounds may be roughly divided into "heavy" chemicals, which serve largely as raw materials in other branches of chemical industry, and "fine" chemicals, which consist mainly of high-priced finished products such as dye-stuffs, drugs, photographic chemicals and the like.

The heavy chemical industries include those concerned with the manufacture of low-priced materials such as sulphuric acid, nitric acid, hydrochloric acid, washing soda and caustic soda, ammonia, bleaching powder and many other inorganic and organic substances which can be produced cheaply and in large quantities. Up to the present the heavy chemical industry has held its own in this country, thanks largely to its careful organisation during the last fifty years by acute scientific minds collaborating with the best procurable business intelligence. The industry is mainly in the hands of a few huge organisations with large capital at their disposal; this condition appears essential to success as securing stability and providing the considerable sums of money often necessary for the development of new working methods. During recent years, however, signs have not been lacking that England's strength in the heavy chemical industries was being seriously challenged; the grounds of the challenge were numerous. One main function of the heavy chemical industry consists in providing the raw materials for the fine chemical industries; these latter have been rapidly passing from English hands and reappearing in Germany vastly increased in magnitude. Early in 1915 Professor Grossmann of Berlin estimated the German exports of fine chemicals at £97,500,000 per annum: the profits on fine chemicals are enormously greater than those on the heavy, but it was plain that Germany would only tolerate the English heavy chemical industry so long as it suited her convenience. Again, the fine chemical industry has developed in Germany in such a manner that the standard heavy chemicals manufactured were in many instances unsuitable as raw materials. Thus, by expending some two millions of money on research the German chemical works had perfected methods for manufacturing indigo from coal tar products; for this purpose sulphuric acid in a more concentrated form than could be made by the customary "chamber" process was required, and German chemists developed a suitable process for preparing so-called "fuming" sulphuric acid by a "contact" process. The contact process had been in use on a small scale in this country for many years. A similar illustration is afforded by the manufacture of artificial indigo, in which liquid chlorine was required in large quantities; a process for preparing and liquefying this gas was worked out on a manufacturing scale by the Badische Anilin und Soda Fabrik, and a very valuable scientific contribution was made to our knowledge of liquid chlorine by Dr Knietsch, a director of these works. The familiarity which the German technologist thus gained in manufacturing and handling liquid chlorine, with the aid of which indigo was made for dyeing our own naval uniforms, led directly to the use of chlorine as an asphyxiating gas during the present war. This particular instance shows how, by the national neglect of such pure chemical research as that directed towards the manufacture of artificial indigo, England has allowed Germany to destroy her once flourishing indigo plantations, to make an inroad on her sulphuric acid industry, and to gain a distinct, if but temporary, military advantage.

## SOAP AND GLYCERINE

This, however, is but a short chapter in the tale. Cheap and plentiful heavy chemicals are the staple nutriment of every chemical industry; the low price of soap in this country is due to cheap caustic soda and to a plentiful supply of vegetable oils from the Colonies. Unless a powerful stream of sulphuric and nitric acids can be pumped throughout the arterial system of the chemical industries distributed throughout the more solid flesh and brain which constitutes a nation, cardiac failure will result. An interesting point arises in this connexion.

Soap is manufactured by boiling vegetable or animal oils and fats with caustic soda; this yields, not only soap, but glycerine. Glycerine, when treated with a mixture of nitric and sulphuric acids, yields nitroglycerine which constitutes about one-half of the British service propellent explosive, cordite. This propellent was invented by the Jacksonian Professor, Sir James Dewar, in collaboration with the late Sir Frederick Abel. Every rifle bullet and every big gun shell used by the Allies or the Central Powers receives its impetus from the explosion of a charge of cordite or some modification of that explosive. The importance of a free supply of animal and vegetable fats for the manufacture of glycerine, to be turned into nitroglycerine, to be made into the standard propellent cordite, is thus apparent; it is not unconnected with the reported shortage of animal fats in Germany and the tardy stoppage of imports of colonial vegetable oils into Central Europe. But the provision of sulphuric and nitric acids is equally important, not only for the manufacture of the propellent cordite, but also for that of the bursting charge, the high explosive, contained in the shell.

Sulphuric acid is manufactured by one of the processes briefly dealt with above. In this country much is made from Spanish iron pyrites; some is produced from native Sicilian sulphur of volcanic origin, but of late years the Sicilian sulphur traffic has become moribund owing to cheaper production of sulphur in America. At the present time none of these sources are open to Germany, and a serious shortage of the raw material from which to produce sulphuric acid has occurred in that country; so important is this question that Germany is now producing sulphuric acid by a necessarily costly process from the gypsum which occurs plentifully in Central Europe. Nitric acid, another essential in the manufacture of cordite, is made in England from Chili saltpetre, crude sodium nitrate, by distillation with sulphuric acid. This source of nitric acid is now closed to Germany, and once more the chemist has been called upon to remedy the deficiency. During many years past German money has been freely expended in utilising the water power available in Scandinavia for bringing about the combination of the nitrogen and oxygen contained in the air and hence producing nitric acid;

# NITRIC ACID

an efficient method for producing nitric acid has thus been developed, but the scale of production, although sufficiently formidable in peace time, does not suffice for war requirements. Since the outbreak of war a process has been perfected in Germany for manufacturing ammonia by the direct combination of nitrogen and hydrogen in very large quantities; further, a method has been elaborated for the economic conversion of ammonia into nitric acid, so that it would appear that the efforts of the German chemists have rendered their country independent of foreign raw materials for the manufacture of nitric acid. As bearing upon this question it may be noted that the military boards of the United States have estimated their requirement of nitric acid, in case of war, at 180,000 tons per annum; this quantity can be produced by utilising another 100,000 horse power out of the 1,000,000 which can still be drawn from the Niagara Falls without affecting the scenic value of the cataract. The economic importance to chemical technology of large supplies of water power is obvious; it is instructive to observe that the Zambesi Falls, situated in British Territory, are capable of a much larger output of energy than those of Niagara.

The intricate manner in which many different national interests are interlocked through the medium of the chemical industries has been already remarked. The close relationship between the artificial production of indigo, the manufacture of sulphuric acid for use in the production of explosives, and the employment of chlorine as a military asphyxiant, has been briefly indicated; but the relationship between chemical industry and national prosperity extends much further. The manufacture of ammonia and nitric acid has just been mentioned; in pre-war days the most important applications of these substances, or their salts, were as artificial manures. This country produces some 450,000 tons of ammonia per annum, chiefly from the distillation of coal, and most of this is used as manure; similarly, much of the British import of Chili saltpetre, which has recently found a competitor in the Scandinavian nitrate, went into the soil. It has been indicated above that Germany has been forced to produce ammonia and nitric acid by new methods for war purposes and it may be anticipated with some confidence that a shortage in these heavy chemicals will be reflected in a light German cereal and tuber harvest this year.

During the past fifty years the German coal tar colour industry has been developed to such perfection, upon a scientific foundation laid entirely in this country, that the production of natural dyestuffs has become insignificant. This is the more striking in that the trade in natural dyestuffs,—indigo, madder, logwood, etc.—was largely in British hands. Germany has taken from us one of the earliest industries of these Islands; the ancient Britons produced indigo for decorative purposes from woad, the cultivation of which still languishes near Cambridge. The cultivation of madder for the production of Turkey red, once a staple industry in France and Turkey, has been killed by competition with the cheaper but identical coal tar product; the Tyrian purple, prepared from time immemorial in Europe and America from a species of snail, is now prepared as a coal tar product. The unpleasant smell of the natural indigo bath and the peaty odour of Harris tweed are made in the German colour factories for the purpose of securing a more hearty welcome from the dyer for the artificial dyestuffs. It is interesting to enquire why this country, which had in its hands the natural dyestuffs, which commanded cheaper raw materials than any other nation, and whose chemists produced the first coal tar dyes both in the laboratory and on a large scale, allowed these enormous assets to pass into Continental hands. The answer is simple; during the past fifty years hardly any English public man of affairs possessing any knowledge of scientific principles has arisen, and no Government Department having the faintest interest in scientific industry has existed. Developments of science, both theoretical and practical, have been greeted with a murmur of surprise, but no authoritative body has been deputed to watch them and to consider how they could be best utilised to the national advantage. Our Continental competitors, less wealthy and more necessitous, had either to seize upon and exploit this British weakness or to remain in penurious obscurity. Germany chose the former alternative, and we now see the English textile industry, amounting to some two hundred millions per annum, embarrassed for lack of a million or so pounds worth per annum of German dyestuffs.

The ignominy of this situation is, however, small in comparison with many other accompaniments of the Continental control of dyestuffs; the war has forced upon us a vast number of other troubles in this connexion, some small and some large. In illustration of one of the smaller kind attention may be called to the treatment of piroplasmosis, one of the most fatal diseases to which domestic and agricultural animals are liable in our tropical colonies; Professor Nuttall explains in this volume that injection with a coal tar dyestuff, Trypan blue, constitutes a fairly certain cure for this otherwise fatal disease. The Trypan blue is produced in the German colour works and supplies are now cut off. Again, photographic plates can be rendered sensitive to the red, yellow and green regions of the spectrum by bathing in dilute solutions of certain dyestuffs; these dyestuffs are made only in Germany and the production of orthochromatic and panchromatic plates, which are largely used in aeroplane photography, is now in jeopardy. These may perhaps be regarded as the pinpricks of the present situation; of enormously

## MANUFACTURE OF EXPLOSIVES

greater importance is the problem presented in connexion with the manufacture of synthetic drugs.

The preparation of many substances invaluable in medicine has been developed on the Continent as an adjunct to the coal tar colour industry; salicylic acid and its derivatives, phenacetin, antipyrine, salvarsan, and several important local anaesthetics, have been imported from Germany at prices so low as to make it impossible for any English manufacturer to compete even if patent monopolies did not exist. The astonishing revival of the fine chemical industry in this country which has occurred during the last two years is gradually making up for the deficiency; it would, however, be of interest to learn to what extent our economies in purchasing such substances cheaply in the past have been obliterated by the enormous cost of smuggling them from Germany since the war began.

The synthetic drug question is not, after all, the most important chemical problem which has arisen during the last two years; the real supremacy in this respect is held by the manufacture of propellent and high explosives. The propellent explosive in every civilised country, cordite or one of its modifications, has been already mentioned above; the high explosives in general use are picric acid and trinitrotoluene. Picric acid is manufactured by treating phenol, separated from coal tar or prepared from coal tar benzene, with mixed nitric and sulphuric acids; trinitrotoluene is similarly manufactured from coal tar toluene. In both cases large quantities of sulphuric and nitric acids are consumed in the manufacture. The plant in every coal tar colour works can be readily diverted from its original purpose, the preparation of colours, to the manufacture of the above high explosives. In August 1914 the plant available in Great Britain for the manufacture of high explosives was hopelessly insufficient for the calls which were to be made upon it, whilst Germany, by issuing an order to its coal tar colour works, could meet any demand upon its resources. In two years this country has been able to remedy all its former deficiencies in high explosive production; it has increased its normal output of one million tons of sulphuric acid per annum to an amount which is doubtless the subject of anxious discussion beyond our fighting line. To do this has necessitated the enlistment of the services of practically every chemical technologist and every academic chemist in the country. A similar result has been achieved in other departments of activity and is, of course, very significant; in provision of explosives, guns, equipment and men, Great Britain has done in two years as much as Germany did in forty years.

An attempt has been made in the foregoing pages to sketch very briefly the way in which one of the most peaceful occupations, that of the chemical technologist, can be rapidly converted into one much more violently aggressive; it is suggested that the wonderful development of the German fine chemical industry has been promoted with this eventuality always in view. This is, of course, a perfectly legitimate view for any State to take, and it behoves others, hitherto careless in such matters, to devise methods for their own future protection. We, in this country, must ask ourselves how any recurrence of the present appalling physical and mental suffering, and dislocation of all productive mental and intellectual work, can be prevented.

The entire fabric of any modern state is built up about the manufacturing and agricultural industries of the country. These and the other more obviously intellectual activities of any Western civilisation are as closely interdependent as are the arterial and nervous systems in the animal body; any deficiency or damage occurring in the one systematic component is speedily reflected in a sympathetic deterioration of some seemingly quite disconnected element of the organism. The public neglect of science in any state is accompanied by poverty of purely intellectual output, by gradual decadence of manufactures, by conservatism of agricultural effort and by the replacement of the statesman by the mere politician; we may indeed anticipate that decay of classical scholarship in our older Universities would have an unfortunate effect upon our science faculties. A strong school always suffers from proximity to a weaker one in a University.

It is probably obvious that the resumption of peace conditions will find each great nation less ready than before to be dependent upon any other for essential products. Preparations for this result are already in progress; thus, whilst the potassium salts essential as agricultural manure have been mainly provided from the salt deposits at Stassfurt, America has recently been particularly active in the search for alternative sources of these materials. One American process for the production of potassium chloride, which consists in roasting potash, felspar, lime and calcium chloride and dissolving out the resulting potassium chloride, professes to produce this salt, of 70 to 80 per cent. purity, for £6 per ton as against a cost of £7. 10s. per ton for the imported German material. Great Britain, like every other large nation, must make itself independent of foreign countries for this and every other essential material. This shortage of potassium salts outside the Central nations, which has resulted in the price of caustic potash advancing from about fourpence to four shillings and six pence per pound, calls attention to what is practically the sole natural resource in raw materials enjoyed by Germany. The Stassfurt salt deposits, the solid residue of the evaporation of some primeval sea, have for many years provided potash salts for the whole world; not because those deposits are unique, for

## GERMAN METHODS

others which should serve the same purpose occur in the British Empire and in America, but because Germany thought it worth while to promote the scientific study of the Stassfurt minerals. One of the most fascinating and intricate chapters in modern Physical Chemistry is that compiled from van 't Hoff's exhaustive experimental and theoretical investigations upon the German salt deposits. It is, however, not impossible that a biological source of the large quantities of potassium salts required will be ultimately found; the ash of the banana stalk contains about 90 per cent. of potassium carbonate and only traces of sodium salts.

Whilst a vast number of directions exist in which the British heavy and fine chemical industry may be developed freely the magnitude of the task of re-establishing the old chemical supremacy enjoyed by Great Britain does not seem to have been generally realised. For the accentuation of this point it may be useful to mention a few striking features presented by one of the important German coal tar product manufactories, that of the Bayer Company of Elberfeld and Leverkusen. So highly developed is the organisation of this concern that it runs free schools of technology, art, and music for its employees and a lying-in hospital for their wives; the company has its own savings bank, life insurance scheme, refectories and dormitories. The Bayer Company, like all the other German fine chemical firms, holds many thousands of carefully drawn up patents; these constitute a valuable asset with which to fight competitors and to conceal actual methods of working. For it must be understood that many of these patents are bogus, that is to say, contain deliberate misstatements for the purpose of misleading enquiring minds as to the manner in which important products are manufactured by the firm. In fact, some German patents are drawn up for the purpose of discouraging investigation by more practical methods; thus, anyone who attempted to repeat the method for manufacturing a dye-stuff protected by Salzmann and Krüger in the German Patent No. 12,096 would be pretty certain to kill himself during the operation. Commercial organisations which have reached such a stage of development as can produce adornments like the above will not suffer much from the kind of competition which we are at present preparing to offer.

The fine chemical industry has been developed to such perfection in Germany as to suggest that independent attempts to establish competing works in this country will encounter formidable difficulties; any new venture will naturally suffer, not only from lack of experience in technical processes, but also from want of an efficient business management. This latter includes, as its most important components, the marketing organisation and a proper costing system; both of these are necessarily of slow and painful growth. These vital essentials are perhaps, however, hopeful signs for the future of the British fine chemical industry. The heavy chemical manufacture in Great Britain is already in the hands of huge concerns in which costing and selling facilities have been very completely developed; it may be anticipated that, with a return to peace conditions, every effort will be made to absorb the fine into the heavy chemical manufactures and with every prospect of success. The command of cheap raw materials, the control of the transport and the existence of means for amalgamating business ability with technical and scientific talent, should diminish the obstacles which confront such an obvious evolutionary process. But the task requires to be taken in hand vigorously and without delay, because other nations are advancing in the same direction; Japan is already sending excellent substitutes for German chemical products into Australia—so perfect is the imitation that much of this merchandise carries, in addition to a Japanese inscription, the words "made in Germany."

An attempt has been made in the foregoing pages to demonstrate the intimacy with which scientific and technological chemical progress are interwoven and to indicate the necessity for wholehearted collaboration of business, technical, and scientific skill in the development of the British fine chemical industry. It is important, however, to consider how the army of skilled chemists which is even now being called for is to be recruited; the country commands an ample supply of latent scientific talent which requires educating, and the development of this ability, formerly allowed to pass into other channels, should receive careful thought. Our public schoolmasters have in the past very wisely attached great importance to the formation of character in their pupils; no educational factor is so potent in ensuring an honourable career and an influential position, and to its existence must be attributed the stupendous changes in modes of thought and action which have taken place in this country during the last two years. But it must be made impossible in the future for our schoolmasters to hold aloof from all the rapidly changing exigencies of modern life. It must be insisted upon that the teacher who allows an intelligent pupil to arrive at man's estate without a good colloquial command of at least two modern languages besides his mother tongue has narrowly limited the youth's outlook on life. How difficult it will be to bring this truth home may be surmised from the fact that one distinguished schoolmaster has for many years found it necessary to preach the doctrine that Latin can be used as a means of human intercommunication and has incurred the censure of some of his colleagues by attempting to teach Latin as if it were a language.

The teaching of science in our schools, which

has been improving so slowly during the last twenty years, must be stimulated and some scientific method of selecting and co-ordinating the science subjects to be taught must be introduced. It would seem rational that mathematics should be the earliest science dealt with, followed by physics, chemistry and mechanics, and that wholly subordinate importance should be attached to the biological sciences, because the elementary stages of these latter subjects are necessarily largely descriptive and insusceptible to broad treatment as illustrative of scientific reasoning and method. That our schools do not keep in view the fundamental scheme which correlates all the natural sciences is obvious; it becomes especially evident when the large amount of time often devoted to botany is contrasted with that allotted to physics and chemistry, particularly in our girls' schools. Elementary botany, as frequently taught in schools, has scarcely any educational value; the botanical work of the last fifty years has been enormously fruitful, but its scientific results are in the main only to be studied by the specialist of wide scientific training.

The introduction into the public school curriculum of proper methods of teaching modern languages and of sound methods of teaching the principles of the fundamental physical sciences would result in an output of young men capable of forming a sound judgment as to what subjects should be their future study. Those who came later to one of our Universities would bring a rational appreciation of the direction in which their own abilities should naturally lead them; the great number of instances with which we are all acquainted of men devoting themselves to entirely unsuitable work would be considerably diminished.

The widening of the educational ambit of the public schools on lines similar to those briefly sketched above must lead to a great increase in the number of science students presenting themselves in our Universities and science Colleges. It will lead, by a process of natural selection, to the classification of men suitable for careers in the many different branches of scientific technology which must shortly develop rapidly in the British Isles. The provision of well-trained men for use in our chemical industries will be assured.

It has been shown in the course of this article that many chemical discoveries which at first appeared to possess a purely philosophical interest have in the past very rapidly become of prime importance as the foundations of new chemical industries. Such chemical discoveries are only to be made by picked men working under comparatively undisturbed conditions; the volume of original chemical research which our science Colleges and Universities have poured out annually in the past needs to be increased. Men who prove themselves especially adapted to purely scientific work must be subsidised in order that they may be able to devote themselves entirely to the task of scientific discovery. The provision of larger numbers of science students must lead to the selection of more men peculiarly fitted for that experimental investigation towards abstract ends which has furnished such gigantic contributions to the world's wealth during the past century. It is impossible to calculate the capitalised value of the alkali industry founded by Leblanc, who committed suicide owing to poverty, or of the chemical industries based on the work of Michael Faraday, who ended his days in comparative comfort on a Civil List pension.

In the future money will have to be provided from public funds for the stimulation and prosecution of chemical research, whether of purely academic or practical technological interest, and in amounts which will bear no comparison with the few thousands of pounds per annum which have been available in the past. It is probably unnecessary to insist further on this matter. The public neglect of science during the last half-century has necessitated immense expenditure on scientific work in the past two years; if recent events have not demonstrated that the national well-being requires the devotion of vast annual sums to the prosecution of scientific research no printed words will make the truth more evident.

# PHYSICAL RESEARCH AND THE WAY OF ITS APPLICATION

By W. H. Bragg, F.R.S.

*Quain Professor of Physics in the University of London.*

Perhaps the need for writing this essay arises from the fact that there is considerable misapprehension of the way in which the discoveries of science are made and applied. It is simple and fascinating to suppose that a new invention is found as complete and clean as a nugget of gold, as unexpected and as unconnected with its surroundings, and finally as readily convertible into cash. The truth is very different. Science does not increase by the constant addition of new facts to old, as a museum collection increases by the addition of new specimens. Science grows like a tree which shoots out new branches continually, and at the same time strengthens the old; twigs become boughs, and boughs become great stems, while the tree is always growing higher into the light and more firmly based below. Science is like a tree also in this,

## THE FRUITS OF SCIENCE

that both need wise cultivation. The nourishment of the tree, its training and its pruning, have their true counterparts in the development of science, and in both cases the fruit comes as the reward of skill and labour. This is the thing which is hard to understand and yet is so important. The fruits of science are first seen when they are brought to market, and it is vaguely supposed that they have been picked up somewhere and somehow in the condition in which they appear. Perhaps they were made by the man who carries the basket. It is not realised that the fruit comes at the end of a long process, and that even a little application of science may be a result of many years of unseen growth and labour. It is not even as simple to develop scientific results as it is to grow fruit in an orchard, because there are restrictions in the former case which have no analogue in the latter. The growth of science is not so much under our command as the growth of a tree.

We may change the analogy and think of scientific research as an army advancing into an unknown country, in which it is not possible to see more than a step or two ahead; and the difficulties are such that only certain lines of advance are reasonably practicable. Progress is made step by step along these lines, one discovery leading to another. New roads can only be made as branches from the old. Those who now march forward can but follow the way as it opens out before them; they have no idea whither they are being led. Were it otherwise research could not be so fascinating. It is in this way that knowledge accumulates, and there is no other way. It is not until it has been acquired that it becomes possible to consider whether or no anything can be done with it.

It is not usually possible to say: Such and such an invention would be useful or helpful or profitable, let us proceed to make it. An invention is usually an application of some scientific discovery. The applications of science are rightly described as such: and there must be a science to be applied. It may not be the science of the organised laboratory, though as a matter of fact it usually is in these days. It may be no more than the scientific observation of some keen mind which notices, reflects, associates and draws conclusions. But whatever the actual source of development, there really has been some knowledge on which to build. We may well set this down as one important principle and proceed to add two more.

A second may be stated in the form that knowledge is not generally acquired for the purpose of making any particular invention. The course of advance is in the main beyond human control. Those who conduct research into the laws of nature know well that their progress is made where it can be made. When the thread of an intricate skein is followed and disentangled, one must follow the

## UNFORESEEN RESULTS

thread wherever it goes; and one cannot say beforehand, I will go in this or that direction. Sometimes a complicated knot puts an end to the unravelling of a certain thread and one picks up another to follow for a time in the hope that some connection between the two will in the end be made plain. It is just so in the research into the phenomena round about us, which is being pursued by the thinkers and experimenters of the world. They may be following many threads but still it is threads that they are following, and they can only move where the threads take them. This is a second principle of great importance.

There is a third point which we must not forget, which is, that possibilities cannot generally be anticipated. We cannot think ahead as to what it will be possible for us to do, except perhaps that we may hope to acquire powers which other beings possess and we do not. Fishes go under water and Jules Verne supposes that we may sometime do the same, and writes a book about it which is all the more interesting because submarines actually do it now. He did not draw a picture of human beings exercising the powers of birds that fly in the air, which is rather curious; probably, even this gifted and most imaginative writer did not anticipate the development of the aeroplane. He described a journey round the moon by a party of adventurers, who travelled in a shell fired from an enormous gun. That was purely a fancy picture; no such powers were given, at the time he wrote the book, to any being; and we are no nearer the realisation of this dream than we were then. The things that are coming, the powers we shall possess in the future, and the insight we shall gain, will be very wonderful; we may be quite sure of that. But we cannot really anticipate, and when we try to prophesy and to imagine we are all wrong. Let us take an illustration from actual experience, and try to imagine the development of a certain invention in the reverse fashion; the fashion which is so often supposed to be the true, and which is absolutely false.

We all know now some of the things which X-rays can do. We know that they permit us to have knowledge of the interior of bodies opaque to ordinary light. In particular the surgeon and physician can now examine the interior of the human body, and they find in the X-rays one of the most valuable tools ever placed within their power. Let us consider the manner of their discovery, and in order to appreciate that, let us first consider very briefly their nature and properties. X-rays are really rays of light, except that they have wave lengths ten thousand times shorter than light which is seen by the eye. They are produced inside a glass bulb, highly evacuated of air, by driving an electric discharge through the bulb. The driving is done by an induction coil, which

## THE PROPERTIES OF X-RAYS 29

requires an electric battery to work it. The discharge strikes a small plate in the centre of the bulb; which plate is made of some highly refractory metal because it might be raised to a very high temperature by the discharge. In fact cooling devices are often necessary. The X-rays radiate in straight lines from the plate, and they pass through all substances more or less. Materials composed of atoms of small weight interfere comparatively little with the kind of X-rays most naturally produced and used, that is to say, they are relatively transparent to the rays. Such substances are wood, cloth, aluminium, skin and muscle. Heavier atoms absorb the rays more highly, so that they do not pass easily through plates of lead or copper, for example; even the bones which contain certain heavy atoms like calcium interpose some obstruction to the passage of the rays. Transparency to X-rays has nothing to do with transparency to light rays; some kinds of glass which do not contain very heavy atoms are fairly transparent, in fact the bulbs themselves are made of such glass. But glass containing the heavy atoms of lead makes a highly efficient absorbing screen. Moreover if the rays are allowed to fall on a photographic plate they so affect it that when the plate is developed it shows marks as if ordinary light had been acting on it. If then the hand is laid flat on a photographic plate wrapped up in a light-tight paper envelope, and an X-ray bulb is placed a foot or so above the hand and made to send out its rays, the plate is acted on in varying degrees. Where nothing but the thin paper is in the way of the rays the effect on the plate is strong. The paper is thin and contains no heavy atoms. Where the rays pass through flesh they are weakened before they get to the plate because the flesh, though it contains no heavy atoms, is sufficiently thick to have a screening effect; consequently there is a shadow on the latter when it is developed. Where the rays have to traverse the bones they are much absorbed, and the action on the plate is small. On the whole there is a weak shadow of the flesh upon the plate, and a strong shadow of the bones within that. These are the effects which the surgeon finds so useful. Before he tries to set the limb, or to cut down to remove a foreign body, he knows exactly what is wrong; he has, indirectly it is true, *seen* the mischief and had time to consider his plans before the moment when he must work quickly and every faculty must be free to do its best. It is a marvellous power to possess.

The rays were discovered in 1896. Suppose that in 1894 the surgical profession had asked if science could furnish the powers just described. We are trying to reverse what actually happened, and to see if things could have taken place as they did "Through the Looking Glass"! Now in the first place we cannot imagine how the profession

## THE DISCOVERY OF X-RAYS 31

would come to think of making such a request. No one at that time had ever conceived the possibility of being able to do a thing which was uncommonly like seeing through a door. It would have been classed with vision of that penetrating kind if it had been proposed; and considered as incompatible with known facts. So indeed it was, if its accomplishment was to be some new act of ordinary vision; but the solution came in an entirely different fashion. The problem was solved indirectly, as so often happens; and for this very reason its solution could not have been expected or asked for. Not only may it be asked why this particular request should be chosen in preference to any other of a thousand requests which could be imagined; but it may be asked how it is to be expected that the request should be conceived at all. There was nothing to make anyone think of asking for such a thing as X-rays.

It is impossible to conceive of progress being made in this order, which is the reverse of the natural course. What happened actually was that Röntgen was one day performing an experiment with a spark passing through a tube very perfectly exhausted of air. As there was a certain amount of light from the spark which was interfering with his work, he covered the tube with opaque material. He found that in spite of his precaution something was issuing from the tube which was able to affect photographic plates in the neighbourhood. The phenomenon was new, and he quickly investigated its main properties; the fact that the bones cast a deeper shadow than the flesh was soon noted, and the application to surgery was obvious. This was the actual march of events. How could it have been reversed? But even if human thought had been able to frame the request in the period before the fundamental experiment, there would still have been an irreversible process in the way. The question put, who could have answered it? Imagine a committee of the greatest scientists of the time meeting to devise experiments for the purpose. It is safe to say that they would not have had any idea of the direction in which they should move, and that with all their knowledge and all the resources of the science of the day at their disposal they would have been helpless. They could not have anticipated the discovery which was to be made shortly afterwards, almost without effort, as a natural development of a well-known line of research.

Lastly, the final experiment of Röntgen's would never have been made except as a natural sequence to a long series of researches which preceded it. Consider for a moment the stock of initiative, of ideas and of apparatus which were available to Röntgen at the time. Why should he have been examining the electric discharge at all? It was because it had long been instinctively felt that in the examination of the electric discharge lay a

## DISCOVERIES PRECEDING X-RAYS

great chance of coming nearer to the secret of the meaning of electricity. The great Maxwell insisted on the importance of this view, and the multiplicity of the researches which have been made on the question is an evidence that experimenters generally have been of the same mind. In many cases no doubt the beauty and varied interests of the experiments have been an inducement to researchers; but that would not have been enough in itself. Such an amount of attention would not have been concentrated on the question had there not been a feeling that important secrets were gradually being disclosed. Let us go backwards along the line of advance in order to be consistent to our plan, which is to show that there is such a line and only one natural way along it.

The particular research of Röntgen was concerned with the attempt to clear up the question of radiation from the seat of electric discharge, which question had been prompted by the result of researches immediately preceding such as those of Lenard and Herz. Lenard had actually found that if he caused an electric discharge to pass through a highly exhausted glass tube, in the walls of which he had inserted a "window" of very thin aluminium foil, and if the window was placed in the right position with respect to the discharge, a very feeble radiation seemed to stream from the window into the air outside. Before him Herz had shown that the same sort of radiation existed within a discharge tube and that it could apparently pass through thin aluminium foil within the tube. The existence of radiations which could pass through sheets opaque to ordinary light was of great importance if it could be shown to be real, and that was why it was of such singular interest when Lenard succeeded in coaxing the rays to come out into the open.

Before the time of Herz were the classical experiments of Sir William Crookes who first experimented on a great scale with this strange radiation. He showed what important properties it possessed; how it streamed in straight lines from the negative terminal from the tube; how it made substances phosphoresce, raised bodies to a red heat when it fell upon them, caused little paddle wheels to turn when it struck the blades, could be turned aside by a magnet, and in general possessed properties so unlike in their aggregate the properties of any other radiation then known, that clearly he had crossed the threshold of a treasure chamber new to science. It may help to ease the difficulty of thinking backwards if we realise that these radiations are an important part of the electric discharge of which we have spoken above. They are not the Röntgen rays but the cause of them; the latter have their origin where the former impinge on matter of any kind, and Röntgen could produce the rays which bear his name, because he was actually producing first the rays of Crookes.

## RÖNTGEN'S WORK

Before Crookes, there were Hittorf, Geisler, Maxwell, De la Rue and many others back to Faraday and beyond, who had studied with interest the electric discharge. When Röntgen did his famous experiments he was but the last of a long line of investigators to each and all of whom is due credit for labour which led to this success. It is important to observe that no one had any inkling of the result; nor could see more than the next step ahead. Never was any experiment performed for the sake of making a particular application, but in all cases each advance was directed along the line disclosed from the vantage point gained by the efforts just made.

Consider again the tools which Röntgen possessed. The main pieces of apparatus were the exhausted bulb, the sparking coil, the battery for working the coil, and the photographic plate. The exhausted bulb was simply a glass envelope from which air had been removed until perhaps a millionth remained. The operation was rendered possible by improvements in air pumps, for which Sir William Crookes was mainly responsible. His own experiments were made possible by the high vacua which he succeeded in obtaining. It is to be observed that he laboured to make these improvements, not in order to carry out his brilliant experiments on electric discharge, but because he wanted to make a high vacuum with which to carry out weighings necessary to a determination of the atomic weight of thallium. He could not have had the slightest idea of the consequences of these improvements when he made them. Not only did they lead to his own discoveries of the radiation already described; but they made possible all sorts of consequences of the greatest importance. Let us mention a few:

(*a*) The electric glow lamps, which are used in millions and whose very existence depends upon the effectiveness of the exhaustion of air.

(*b*) The X-ray bulb with all its powers.

(*c*) The vacuum or "thermos" flask, which has made it possible to preserve liquefied gases and to study their properties. This work again has its important developments in pure science, in the purification of materials, in the illumination that has followed on the extension of our knowledge of the properties of bodies at very low temperature and so on.

(*d*) The so-called "valve," which is greatly used at the present time to multiply telephonic sounds, so that they become audible.

Let us take another of Röntgen's tools, the sparking coil. Its history is not so varied as that of the research on the electric discharge, but it is of even greater importance, if that is possible. It consists merely of two coils of wire wound on the same iron core, the one having a few turns of thick wire, the other many turns of thin wire. Interruptions of the electric current running in the thick coil cause such electric forces in the thin, that sparks leap across the terminals of the latter. The arrangement is often called by Rhumkorff's name, though actually he was anticipated a year or two by Henry in America. And before this the first steps were made almost simultaneously by Henry in America and Faraday in England. These two great experimenters both laid bare the surprising and unexpected actions of currents upon one another. If we may move for a moment in the proper direction, it was Maxwell who co-ordinated this and other experiments of Faraday's, and drew conclusions which led to the recognition of light as an electrical phenomenon, to the understanding of electric oscillations, to the anticipation of the existence of electric waves, to their experimental realisation by Herz, to their examination by Righi, Lodge, Marconi and others, and so finally to their application on a great scale, chiefly through the ability of Marconi, to wireless telegraphy. And here again it is to be said that until this particular result of the long series of researches was reached, no one had any idea of what was coming. Wireless telegraphy is not an "invention" standing alone and conceived apart from all other researches; it is a by-product of a consistent and consecutive system of enquiries; the fruit of many men's work. The researches by which it was achieved do not even stand by themselves; they are inextricably woven with others which led and are leading to results of very different character but of equal importance.

So also we might take the history of the photographic plate through all its stages, which would bring into our view an entirely different line of advance, and force us to recognise all that chemistry had to give before Röntgen's experiment could be done. And we might take the electric battery and allow our minds to recall the numbers who have studied it during the last century, and the enormous extent of its application.

The experiment then, when it is considered in detail, illustrates all the more fully the principles stated at the beginning of this chapter. There is a sequence of events which cannot be reversed. In that sequence discovery follows on discovery; and science must be pure in the sense that each step is necessarily free from any knowledge of what advantage may be made of it. The step is made, not because this or that consequence will be profitable, but because it is the next step on the only way. Science cannot be applied until there is science to apply, and science must begin as pure science. That is why it is impossible to conceive of the development of applied science as apart from pure. It is not even possible to say that now at this moment there is enough pure science, and we may henceforth devote ourselves to applying what we have. Such present neglect must only lead to future sterility. The very experi-

## PURE AND APPLIED SCIENCE

ments of the day in pure science may be those which are immediately ready for fruitful application.

It is not even wise to separate pure and applied science too widely; it is profitable to keep them in close touch. Pure science may be developed by itself, but it is the gainer if its workers are alive to the inspiration which is to be found in watching its application. Chemists, physicists, geologists, all scientific experimenters, know this well enough, in these days at any rate. On the other hand applied science does suffer most materially if there is any attempt to cut away pure science as unnecessary. Here again workers and experimenters are alive to the situation, and do their best to keep in touch with their fellows through literature and societies. But it is not clear that this point is always understood by those who have the power to encourage the development of science. Educational authorities and directors of industry are to be commended who, when they erect institutions for the imparting of applied and technical knowledge, see to it that pure science is encouraged as well.

There is a general feeling in this country at the present time that the alliance between industry and science must be more firmly drawn. It is to be observed that the science which is to be woven into industry and is to give it life and the power of growth and adaptation, is the pure science of which we have spoken. There *is* no other. There is no applied science distinct from pure science; there are applications of pure science, that is all. The existence of this general feeling is real enough. It is shown everywhere, in public speeches, newspaper articles, private conversations; and it meets with little contradiction. Let us by all means turn it to good advantage; and to do so we must give it understanding. We wish to hasten the process by which scientific discoveries are made and applied; but we must understand which way the wheels go round when the machine works and try to urge them in that way. The natural machinery is there, right enough. The danger is lest we all sit round it and poke levers and hooks into it in various places and all push and pull without a general purpose. We need to appreciate the natural method of working if we are to make the machine work well.

That is why it is necessary to emphasise the fact that pure science must come first, in point of time at least. We must always press forward to acquire, and to continue acquiring knowledge. It is no good calling it useful knowledge; because when it is first got, no one knows whether it ever will be useful. And after that we have to see that we encourage all means by which it can be made useful. These two sides of the question may be considered quite separately. The acquisition of knowledge—the first aim—is most simply promoted by financial encouragement to institutions

## STARVING OF SCIENTIFIC RESEARCH 41

at which research work is carried on. Money can be given to provide books and tools and apparatus, and, still more important, time. It is already given to some extent in England; but that which is given to provide for scientific research is minute in comparison with the huge amounts derived from the development of the results of research.

On Christmas Day, 1821, Michael Faraday, who had been working on a previous experiment by Oersted made in 1819, called his wife into his laboratory to see, for the first time, a magnet going round an electric current. That was the first of all the electric motors. It would be hard to say how many millions, nay thousands of millions, the electric motor has added to the wealth of the world. But it is quite safe to say that no more than a small fraction of one per cent. of that sum has gone back to encourage further research.

In a paper in the *Scientific Monthly* of November, 1915, Professor T. Brailsford Robertson quotes census returns showing that the annual value of manufacturing industries in the United States developed from patented scientific invention was, in 1909, about eighty millions sterling. He adds that in 1913 the whole income of all the higher institutions of learning in the States was about eighteen millions sterling, of which a minute percentage was expended in research. Any corresponding figures for the United Kingdom would certainly be far worse. Strike out all processes and manufactures, all human operations in which the laws of heat or light or sound or electricity play a part, and consider what a blank there would be in our work and our lives. Electric light, electric motors, telegraph and telephone, steam engines and gas engines, the photographic camera, the microscope and the telescope, the work of the oculist, all these details are obvious and direct. But in a thousand other ways, in the details of a bridge or a house, a ship or an aeroplane, of a chronometer or a motor, or any construction one likes to name, these great sciences must continually be consulted. Without them there would be little or nothing. In a sense the work of the world animate and inanimate goes on by their leave, and the more we know of them, the more we can appreciate all that we see and hear.

Yet all we know of these laws has been discovered as "pure" science, that is to say in the course of a quest which was not directed to any special discovery or invention or application. We must not starve, therefore, the research into pure science. We must provide the time and money for research laboratories and institutions, and we must do so on a far more liberal scale than in the past. And first of all perhaps, it is time that must be paid for. Those who are able to investigate are so often found in positions which absorb the bulk of their time and energy for teaching and management. They are accustomed to work

## APPLICATION OF PURE SCIENCE 43

with poor apparatus and tools. The need is for better equipment and more assistance.

That is the first thing, to provide for the encouragement of research and the growth of pure science. Then the second question arises: when we have got it, how shall we encourage its application? As a nation we fail rather in our quickness to do so. Why is not more use made of science in England? It cannot fairly be said that we lack the ability to study and discover. On the contrary, the records of science show that a very large proportion of the physical discoveries that matter are made in the British Empire, and of late years this has been especially true. This is not said as a boast but as a contribution to a clear view of our position. We should be as wrong to overlook our sources of encouragement as our reasons for blame. Therefore it is right to take as an example a new science like radio-activity, in which all nations started from the same mark. With one or two exceptions such as Mme Curie's original separation of radium, nearly every experimental fact of importance has been discovered within the Empire. Doubtless there are several contributing causes to our neglect of the opportunities of applying scientific discoveries. But there are two which we may well consider in this present connection. The first is that we have been as a nation so well off, our factories so full of work and orders, that we have settled down comfortably into a lazy feeling that we are doing well and need not worry. We have rested on our oars. Younger nations have had to fight for what has come to us by tradition; and they have been more keenly alive to the need for constant improvement in method, and the danger of overlooking any development of knowledge which might give greater power.

The second cause concerns us more nearly. It is that there is no sufficient general understanding of what science is, of what it can do and, it may be added, of what it can not do. So much has been said and written on this matter since the beginning of the war, that it is unnecessary to labour the point now. It is enough to say that there is a general agreement as to the unfortunate and mistaken attitude which is so commonly displayed towards scientific work. It is not that there is any lack of admiration for scientific results; wonder and applause are forthcoming to an extent which is often distressingly exaggerated. The trouble is that the feeling stops there. There is a curious mixture of humility and pride which is very depressing. Humility shows itself in an apparent resignation to the existence of a great breach between ordinary people and these scientific men who talk familiarly of things almost incomprehensible. There is no great breach at all; it is all the more difficult to cross because it is a fancy, bred of a wrong tradition and, perhaps it may be added, of laziness. The pride comes in when it is said that after all scientific work smacks of materialism and that the God whom we would worship is a spirit. It is true that science works with brain and hand; it is not true that its aims are unspiritual.

After all this is the real point at issue. Latin and Greek, Philosophy and History are to many the mainstay of education; science is an extra like dancing. The humanities would show the relations between man and man, and between man and his God. Science is a cold collection of soulless facts. If that were all, then indeed there would be no plea for science. But it is not so; on the one hand science is a living growing thing, full of human triumphs and failures; on the other hand it is an equipment necessary for the man who would live and help as he should. All the humanities of the world centre in the two great commandments of the Christian religion; if it is the business of the humanities to honour and set forth these commandments it is the part of science to furnish the equipment for carrying them out. This is the idea which must be recognised before we can hope to change the general attitude, and in particular the educational attitude, to science. We have to destroy the idea that we would substitute something sordid and material for that which is spiritual and noble. To point to the material usefulness of science will only bring a reluctant consent to its full admission into educational schemes, and that is as it should be. We desire that science should be welcomed gladly, and we believe it deserves such a welcome because it is necessary to the man who would do his best, and because it is itself one of the greatest of human interests.

That is why one has need to beware of what is meant by the substitution of science for classics in the education of our schools. It is utterly dismal and wearisome to spend one's days on the intricacies of declensions and conjugations, on the exceptions to rules of grammar and the niceties of first and second aorists. It is no less miserable to force one's memory to absorb lists of scientific data and modes of experimentation. Nothing is to be gained by replacing one drudgery for the other. There may be a very serious loss. Speech after all is human speech, and the old Latin and Greek words have served to express the minds of men in times of achievement and hope, of failure and despair; they have carried the great truths which men have won, and all their sentiments. They are like old machinery, worn and moulded by use, every mark on them the witness of their service. If we do no more than make a study of the marks and count the scratches we make idiots of ourselves. But if we think of what it all means, we move forward in our education. I think that as boys at school we may have instinctively felt that our teachers had seen the greater things even though some of us may have wondered

## THE HUMAN SIDE OF SCIENCE     47

dumbly and without understanding why the grammar which we learnt seemed so meaningless and so dull. Unless we were unfortunate in our teachers we learnt to look past the spoken word to the thoughts and habits that moulded it.

No study really grips the mind and interest of the learner unless it has something human about it. We are interested when a risk is run for the sake of an object which cannot otherwise be obtained; fascinated by the efforts and sacrifices of faith. Science also has its tale of such efforts and sacrifices: furthermore it is always young, interested in its growing powers and in the mysteries of its future. On the one hand, then, let us avoid even the appearance of ingratitude to the teachers and the studies that made us aware of the heroisms in the great struggle of humanity. It has been the glory of our public schools that they have taught the meaning of faith and self-sacrifice, and of devotion and unity. That can never be taken from them. Let us say what we think about the neglect of science and the strange indifference to the knowledge of how best to do things, and of the tools with which we may do them. Nevertheless we will not forget our debt.

We must be careful as to what we take away, and what we put in its place. We may prune away hours that have borne little fruit, and have been spent overabundantly on the niceties of grammar and phrases. We may put in their place time given to the laws and facts that touch us very nearly. On the other hand let us not forget that the science which is worthy of a place in a school must show itself to be alive. It is not a mere training in manipulative skill nor the setting forth of a collection of dead facts and dogmatic statements. There is not a fact or a law in the whole of science which is in its finished form. Growth and change are everywhere. The story must deal with the work of the past, and the successes and failures of the men who have laboured to advance it. It must show also that the advance of science is never ended, and make clear its eager and expectant attitude towards the future. Let our young men catch the spirit and swing of the onward march, and they will not stand idle while opportunities slip past unobserved.

# THE MODERN SCIENCE OF METALS, PURE AND APPLIED

By Walter Rosenhain, F.R.S.

*Superintendent, Metallurgy Department, National Physical Laboratory.*

As a concrete example of the most far-reaching practical results flowing from purely scientific investigation, the modern achievements of Metallurgy occupy a unique position. The events of the Great War cannot fail to impress upon all thinking minds the fundamental importance of metallurgical products, since it is upon them in the first instance that the very existence of the nation, which has to rely upon military and naval equipment, is seen to depend. In the arts of peace also, the whole fabric of modern progress is based upon an adequate and cheap supply of metals. So much is this the case that it may fairly be said that the principal technical advances of the last hundred years could not have taken place had not the inventions of Bessemer and Siemens created the "age of steel."

Metallurgy is, further, of particular interest from the present point of view because, while in itself one of the oldest—if not *the* oldest—of the technical arts, the science associated with it is of extremely modern growth. The older metallurgical inventions, among which—in this age of rapid technological development—those of Bessemer, Siemens and Thomas-Gilchrist can already be reckoned, are based upon the fundamental principles of Chemistry and Physics. The working of the Bessemer Converter involves a chemical phenomenon, viz. the combustion of the carbon contained in molten iron by means of air which is blown through the molten mass. The Siemens regenerative furnace, again, is a brilliant application of the laws of heat discovered by investigators in pure Physics. The science upon which these things are based, however, is general Chemistry and Physics rather than a specific science of "Metals." The older "Metallurgy" was, so far as its purely scientific aspect was concerned, simply the direct application of the known laws of Chemistry and Physics to the processes employed in the production of metals from their ores. During the past fifty years, however, and principally during the past thirty years, a New Metallurgy has grown up with amazing rapidity. This new science has sprung from purely scientific investigations and has been largely pursued for its own sake, and for the sake of general conclusions which should

## THE NEW METALLURGY

throw light on the wider questions of Physics and Physical Chemistry in relation to the nature and constitution of matter. Yet, parallel with this development of a new science, there has occurred an unprecedented advance in the metallurgical art, and there can be no doubt that we have here a definite connection of cause and effect—that the surprisingly rapid advance of metallurgical practice, occurring at a stage when so much had already been achieved that it was hard to imagine where further progress could be made, is the direct result of this new development in the investigation of metals for their own sake. A brief review of these parallel developments will serve as a striking example of the manner in which purely scientific research brings about, both directly and indirectly, practical results of the highest value.

The birth of the New Metallurgy is rightly dated from the work of H. C. Sorby who in Sheffield, in the year 1861, first applied the microscope to the study of metals. Although he worked in Sheffield, Sorby was not a metallurgist but a mineralogist, and by introducing the microscopic study of rock-sections he first laid the foundations of modern petrography. His devotion to this science, which even to this day has found few direct practical applications and is—rightly—pursued for its own sake, shows how little Sorby himself had practical ends in view when, seeking further insight into the nature of meteorites, he applied to these pieces of extra-terrestrial metal the methods of microscopic examination which he had successfully developed for the study of rocks. The nature of metals—that they cannot be cut into sections or slices sufficiently thin to be transparent, so that the optical methods of petrography cannot be applied to them, forced Sorby to develop new and beautiful methods for their microscopic examination. He thus evolved the technique of preparing metal surfaces by first polishing them very perfectly and then "etching" them by attacking them with an acid. This mode of attack produces a surface pattern of great clearness and beauty which reveals the internal structure of the metal. This method has formed the foundation for one of the most important branches of the New Metallurgy, but how little its practical importance was realised even in Sheffield—which claims to be the home of all that is best in Metallurgy—is shown by the fact that Sorby's work lay neglected and forgotten until it was revived by the independent initiative of two continental workers—Osmond in France and Martens in Germany. Yet at the present time, all metallurgical works of any importance have their metallographical laboratories where the methods of Sorby are daily practised for the control of industrial operations.

While the new instrument of investigation which was placed in the hands of metallurgists by Sorby has contributed very largely to the growth of the

# THERMO-ELECTRICITY

New Metallurgy, that growth could have been neither so rapid nor so sound had it not been for the co-operation of another and entirely different method of studying metals. This also had its beginning in purely scientific research, dating back to the earlier part of the nineteenth century, when the "thermo-electric" properties of metals were first studied by physicists. The fundamental discovery in this case was a purely electrical one —it consists in the simple fact that where two pieces of different metals touch one another, the application of heat produces a small electric current—provided that the pieces of metal are connected together so as to form a complete electric circuit. Take the simplest case, of two pieces of wire of different metals joined together at both ends so as to form a closed loop. In such a loop there are two "junctions" where the two metals come into contact. If now one of these junctions is kept cold while the other is heated, a small electric current is caused to flow around the loop. If the second junction were to be equally heated, an equal but opposite electric flow would be produced and the two currents would neutralise one another; in this way the actual amount of current which flows around such a circuit is in reality a measure of the difference of temperature between the two junctions. Attempts to obtain practical applications of these facts were soon made; in one direction it was endeavoured to utilise the electric current thus produced, but the resulting electric "thermo-piles" never attained much importance. In another direction, however, great success was achieved by utilising this property of junctions of dissimilar metals for the construction of sensitive instruments for detecting slight changes of temperature. Further study of the subject—among others by P. G. Tait in Edinburgh—led finally to the invention by Henri Le Chatelier of the thermo-electric pyrometer for measuring high temperatures. Le Chatelier introduced the use of a thermo-couple or pair of wires consisting of pure platinum and of platinum alloyed with ten per cent. of either rhodium or iridium. The junctions of these wires can, with suitable precautions, be exposed to temperatures as high as 1600° C. (an intense white heat) without injury or excessively rapid deterioration, such as would occur with metals like copper or iron which would either melt or rapidly burn away. Le Chatelier's thermo-couple can therefore be used for the accurate measurement of high temperatures. At first sight it appeared that the principal use of such an instrument would lie in its direct application to industrial furnace practice, where a ready means of accurately measuring high temperatures would furnish a new method of regulating and controlling those operations. To some extent this has been the case, but the cost and fragility of the instruments required have acted as a serious handicap for this application

# IRON AND STEEL

and in recent times other methods for measuring industrial high temperatures have been evolved and perfected. But the highest service which Le Chatelier's thermo-couple has rendered has been as an instrument for purely scientific investigation, as an aid to that study of the structure and constitution of metals and alloys which was rendered possible by the advent of the microscopic examination of metals.

Having seen how the new methods of studying metals originated, we may now consider what is the kind of new knowledge about metals which the application of these methods has revealed. This we can attempt only in the broadest outline, since the new science already constitutes a subject of such magnitude that the workers in it are finding it necessary to specialise upon some part of its field. It must be stated at the outset, too, that this is not a case in which the subject was first allowed to develope on purely scientific lines, but that at every stage attempts were made to apply and utilise in practice the results obtained in the laboratory. There can be no doubt that the development of the whole subject was to some extent hindered, both on the practical and the scientific side, by some of these premature attempts. As it happens, that metal which from the practical point of view stands in importance so far above all others—iron—is also the most difficult and complex to deal with from the point of view of the

New Metallurgy. While it was only natural that iron and its alloy—steel—should be chosen as the first subjects for attack by the new methods, both for scientific and practical purposes, yet the result has been somewhat unfortunate, as it led to an attack being made on the most difficult problems before experience had been gained in dealing with the simpler questions. The result has been that in regard to iron and steel the progress of the New Metallurgy has been shrouded in a cloud of controversy and misconception which has greatly interfered with its steady advancement. The growth of the new science, and its practical applications, has, even so, been astonishingly rapid; had it been possible to allow a sound scientific foundation to be laid before complex practical problems were attacked, some mistakes and set-backs would certainly have been avoided. This aspect of the history of the subject serves as a much-needed warning that "research" undertaken with a directly practical object may actually hinder progress rather than assist it. Gradually, however, the sound development of the subject on true scientific lines has overtaken most of the earlier false starts, so that a clear view of the whole subject together with its effects on metallurgical technology is now possible. Essentially, the New Metallurgy has provided us with an entirely new and in large measure unexpected insight into the inner structure and constitution of metals and alloys, and with detailed knowledge of the changes and transformations which these materials undergo as the result of heating and cooling or of mechanical treatment. While we cannot, obviously, follow out the details of the great mass of new knowledge thus obtained, there are a few of the wider generalisations which can, perhaps, be sufficiently explained to afford an insight into the inter-action of the new knowledge with technical practice.

When a piece of a pure metal, such as copper, gold or silver, has been properly prepared by polishing and etching and is then examined under the microscope, a very characteristic "pattern" or structure is seen—a structure which is extremely similar in all pure metals. The surface of the metal is seen to be mapped out into a number of roughly polygonal areas which appear to be divided from one another by fine black lines; the surface has the appearance of a fine mosaic pavement consisting of somewhat irregular pieces very beautifully fitted together. The sizes of the individual grains of this mosaic vary widely according to the rate at which the particular piece of metal has been cooled from fusion; thus in lead, when slowly cooled, they may be large enough to be readily seen with the unaided eye, while in rapidly-cooled iron they may be so small that two hundred of them placed side by side would scarcely measure an inch. It has been shown, however, that each of these grains —for the polygonal areas seen on a prepared surface are merely the sections of polygonal grains or particles—are really small crystals of the metal. These crystals are quite as truly crystals as the beautiful and perfectly geometrical pieces of rock-crystal or alum or sugar with which we familiarly associate that term; they have, however, grown up together and the growth of each, instead of finding room to complete itself to full geometrical perfection, has been limited by the presence of its neighbours. The polygonal boundaries which we see in our sections are thus merely the accidental surfaces upon which adjacent growing crystals came into contact with one another.

This fact alone—that metals are aggregates of an immense number of minute crystals—constituted a discovery of fundamental importance, particularly when it came to be shown how these crystals behave when the metal is subjected to mechanical deformation—such as bending or stretching—and ultimately to fracture. While crystals of salt or sugar are fairly hard, they are very brittle—any attempt to bend or squeeze or stretch them either fails to produce any permanent change of shape or causes immediate fracture. The crystals of many metals, however, are quite easily deformed—they can be squeezed or stretched; the mechanism by which they undergo deformation, however, is of a peculiar kind. Each crystal undergoes a change of shape in the first place merely by a process of slipping which in itself leaves the structure of the crystal

## DEFORMATION AND SLIP IN CRYSTALS  59

essentially unchanged—whole layers of the crystal slide over one another bodily, and by a sufficient number of such slidings the crystal can adapt itself to the new shape imposed upon it. The way in which the slipping of layers, which themselves remain unchanged in size and shape, can alter the shape of the whole pile is readily seen by piling a number of books upon one another; if now each book is pushed slightly to one side, the pile as a whole becomes very much changed in shape, although each individual book remains unchanged. If this slipping constituted the whole of the process, then we should expect that mechanical change of shape would not materially alter the properties of a piece of metal. Actually, however, we find that its properties are very much changed. If a piece of ductile copper, for instance, be drawn out into wire, it gradually increases in strength and hardness but loses in ductility until finally it becomes so brittle that it can be drawn out no further without breaking. The causes of this hardening have been studied, and it has been found that the reason lies in the fact that on the surfaces where crystal layers slide over one another the intimate structure of the crystal itself becomes disturbed. The mere process of polishing the surface of a crystal—whether of metal or of other material—is found to be sufficient to disturb and more or less to destroy the crystalline structure of a layer of appreciable depth, so that it is not surprising to find that where two adjacent crystal layers move over one another under the heavy pressures which must exist within a metal undergoing plastic deformation, similar but more intense disturbance occurs. The essence of crystalline structure is the regular arrangement of the atoms on certain geometrical patterns which allow —among other things—of the existence of "gliding planes" or surfaces upon which this sliding of layers can take place. Where the sliding has actually taken place, however, this regular arrangement is locally destroyed and with it the "gliding planes." Further gliding is thus rendered more difficult and the metal appears to be harder but also more brittle than before. Gradually, as the crystalline structure becomes more and more deeply disturbed, no power of gliding remains, and if sufficient force is applied the crystal—or such remnants of it as remain—breaks without further change of shape; in this state the metal is hard and brittle and behaves in much the same way as a material like glass, which is devoid of any regular structure.

Up to this point we have followed in outline the course of a purely scientific discovery, none the less purely scientific in character because it deals with the inner meaning of phenomena which occur in daily technological practice, when metals are "worked" in the cold into many complicated shapes. We shall now see how a result of the

## "FATIGUE STRESS"

greatest practical value has sprung out of this purely theoretical knowledge. This relates to the failure of metals under what is called "fatigue" and to the methods available for preventing these failures. Suppose a round bar of iron to be fixed horizontally—firmly held at one end and projecting freely at the other. Now let a load be hung to the free end; if this load is steadily increased, the bar will at first bend and ultimately it will break. Now instead of increasing the load to the point where fracture occurs, let us stop at the stage when the bar has just begun to bend a very little. In this state, the bar would continue to support the same load, without appreciable further bending, for an indefinite time. If, however, we were to remove the load and then to re-apply it in quick succession, the bar would break after some thousands of repeated applications. The experiment is usually made by leaving the load hanging from the bar but rotating the bar; in that way opposite sides of the bar come into play in turn as the bar revolves and the effect is the same as that of leaving the bar stationary and reversing the load repeatedly. Such an alternating or intermittent load is known as a "fatigue stress" and frequently occurs in the moving parts of machinery, where the direction of loading is sometimes reversed many hundred times per minute. Pieces of metal subjected to such conditions frequently fail under loads which they could bear indefinitely if left at rest. Now this is a matter of the highest practical importance, and a remedy can only be found when the reason for this apparent "fatigue" is known. It so happens that the fracture which results from such a case of fatigue often exhibits curiously bright crystalline facets, and it was long supposed that the cause of the failure was due to the metal changing from a supposed normal "fibrous" to a supposedly abnormal, weak and brittle "crystalline" condition. But the New Metallurgy has already taught us that the metal is essentially crystalline to begin with, and that its crystalline nature is not inconsistent with strength and ductility; microscopic examination of pieces which have failed under "fatigue" next serves to show most clearly that their structure has not undergone any change of that kind—they are neither more nor less crystalline than before. The old "explanation," therefore, is entirely disproved; what, then, is the correct explanation?

It is really very simple, and arises naturally out of the fact that when metal undergoes plastic deformation—as when our bar is even slightly bent under its load—this occurs by slipping of layers within some of the component crystals of the metal. If this slip is left undisturbed—*i.e.* if the load is left quietly on, then nothing further occurs. If, however, the load is reversed, a new series of events begins. The reversal of the load tends to reverse the process of slipping by which

# FAILURE UNDER "FATIGUE"

the crystals have accommodated themselves to the load, and on some of the surfaces actual reversal of the slip takes place each time the load is reversed. Now at each time of slipping there is, as we have already seen, a considerable disturbance of the crystalline arrangement near the surface of slip, and when this slipping is continually reversed this disturbance becomes an actual process of attrition. The whole process has been watched under the microscope, and what happens after a certain time is that the surface of continual slipping developes into an actual fissure or crack. The next step is that, since this particular crystal has been thrown entirely out of action, a greater proportion of the total load is thrown upon its immediate neighbours and the process of slip-reversal and attrition takes place in them. In this fashion the flaw or crack started within—perhaps—a single crystal, works its way through the entire piece of metal with increasing rapidity until fracture results. This fracture naturally shows the crystal-facets upon which the slip-reversals have taken place and thus exhibits the typical "crystalline" appearance of such fatigue fractures.

This explanation of the process of failure by "fatigue" is in itself simply a further step in the scientific explanation of phenomena met with in practice; it is the third or fourth step in a chain of purely scientific discoveries, and it is only at this stage that practical application becomes apparent. An insight into the mechanism of fatigue failures at once opens up the possibility of avoiding their disastrous incidence. Fatigue fracture results from reversals of slip in individual crystals of a piece of metal; if we avoid the occurrence of such slip in the first instance, the whole chain of events leading to ultimate fracture is prevented. From this follows the simple practical rule that if any piece of metal is to resist the alternating application of a load for an indefinite number of times, this load must not be large enough to produce even a slight amount of slip in any of the minute constituent crystals of the metal. Now slip occurs so soon as the metal undergoes even the slightest plastic or permanent change of shape; expressed in technical terms this fact is stated by saying that slip occurs so soon as the elastic limit is passed. Up to this "elastic limit," when the load is removed the metal returns to its original shape—the metal has merely been elastically deformed; but so soon as this limit is passed, the metal retains a permanent—although possibly very minute—change of shape. The problem is thus reduced to determining with great care and accuracy the intensity of loading which a given metal can bear without passing this elastic limit and then so arranging matters that the loads applied in service never exceed this value. To that extent our discovery leads to a practical engineering rule of the highest importance; it takes us a good deal further, however, for close study of this problem has shown very clearly that the value of this "elastic limit" depends very much upon the nature of the metal in question, and even for a given kind of metal —such as any particular grade of steel—its value depends upon the exact treatment which the metal has undergone. Our knowledge of the crystalline structure of metals here helps us again. Plastic deformation takes the form of slip within the crystals, but the individual crystals are not free to undergo slip or to resist it without reference to their neighbours, and the manner and extent to which a given crystal is interlocked with its neighbours and supported by them will determine the load which it can bear before slip commences. An isolated crystal standing by itself receives no support from neighbours; in a piece of metal consisting of large crystals, the amount of support which these can afford one another is small, but in a metal consisting of a very large number of very minute crystals, slip occurs with much greater difficulty, since movement in any one individual crystal can only take place by the aid of a complicated system of mutual adjustments involving a very great number of crystals. Observation shows clearly that a metal having a fine structure invariably exhibits a higher elastic limit and a correspondingly greater resistance to fatigue than a metal of the same chemical composition having a coarse structure. Fortunately it is possible to carry the matter very much further. The combined use of the microscope and the pyrometer in the study of metals has revealed the fact that the structure of a given piece—particularly in the case of steel—can be readily varied by the effects of mechanical and thermal treatment; the whole scale and character of the structure can be altered by such means as heating to specific temperatures followed by cooling at a specific rate. In this way it is possible specially to prepare our metals not only to resist fatigue but also to meet many other requirements. Once this has been understood—that the internal structure of metal governs its physical properties, and that the internal structure can be modified and controlled by methods which the New Metallurgy has enabled us to specify, we have the key to one of the most important of modern metallurgical developments. In iron and steel—and more particularly in those special steels, containing nickel, chromium and vanadium, which are so largely used in the production of guns, armour plate, and many other forms of modern equipment, both military and civil, this matter of heat-treatment has become of paramount importance. The best and most expensive types of steel which are employed for such purposes become useless if wrongly treated —if heated or cooled or quenched from the wrong temperature or if subsequently re-heated or "tem-

# THERMAL PHENOMENA

pered" for too long a time or at too low or too high a temperature. All these processes are the direct outcome of the purely scientific study of the structure and constitution of metals and alloys.

This aspect of our subject is so important that it is worth while following it back to its beginnings. These lie, as has already been indicated, in the combination of the thermal study of metals, by means of the Le Chatelier thermo-couple, with the study of the micro-structure. In its simplest form the thermal study of metals and alloys consists merely in determining the melting or freezing points. Even these, when taken for a whole series of alloys between two metals and plotted in the form of a "melting-point" curve, form a diagram which is of considerable interest. This melting-point curve, however, is but the first step in an investigation of such a series of alloys, because it is found that at temperatures very much below the melting-point many metals and alloys exhibit thermal phenomena of a most interesting kind. The best-known of these occurs in ordinary carbon steel. If a piece of such steel is heated to bright redness and then allowed to cool, it is seen to cool down steadily until apparently just below visible redness—and then the temperature suddenly rises again and a brief but bright red glow passes over the steel. This is a striking example of the kind of phenomenon which is by no means uncommon in metals and alloys—on

5—2

cooling down to some definite temperature an evolution of heat occurs which temporarily arrests the rapid fall of temperature or—in a few special cases—may be sufficiently violent actually to raise the temperature again. While in steel this effect is strong enough to be visible to the eye, in many metals and alloys it is necessary to employ the thermo-couple with the most delicate electrical measuring instruments in order to detect and locate these "transformation" points. When all such points have been observed in an alloy series, it becomes possible to plot the results in the form of a diagram—known as the "equilibrium" or "constitutional" diagram, which represents in a graphic form all the changes and different conditions to which the various alloys of that system are subject at different temperatures. Such a diagram cannot, however, be satisfactorily drawn solely from observations made with the thermo-couple; it is necessary to call in the aid of the microscope to explain the real meaning of the various lines and areas of these diagrams. This is possible because it is found that with practically every such "transformation" or "critical" point there is associated a well-marked change of micro-structure. It is true that as a rule we can only study the structure of a piece of metal after it has been allowed to cool down, but fortunately it is found that if a specimen is "quenched" or chilled very rapidly it can be more or less completely

## THE HARDENING OF STEEL 69

retained in the condition of structure which it possessed at the moment of quenching. The high-temperature structure as it exists above a critical point can thus be more or less completely preserved by quenching and can then be studied at leisure. But by thus preserving the structure which the metal possesses naturally at a high temperature, and by rapid cooling preventing the transformation which it would undergo if cooled slowly, we also preserve to some extent the physical properties corresponding to that high-temperature condition. The most striking case of this kind is that of steel containing something like one per cent. of carbon which undergoes the violent heat-evolution during cooling to which we have already referred. If this steel is allowed to cool slowly and to undergo the transformation from which that heat-evolution arises, it is fairly soft and tough; if, on the other hand, it is quenched in water from a red heat, in such a way as to suppress as completely as possible that same transformation, then the steel is extremely hard and brittle, and we find a corresponding difference in the micro-structure. To this extent the New Metallurgy has afforded an "explanation" of the oldest of metallurgical mysteries—the hardening of steel. But this is only a particularly striking and familiar case of what is really a widespread class of phenomena. The thorough scientific investigation of all these phenomena is one of the tasks which the New

Metallurgy has set itself; since alloys may be made of the majority of metals taken two, three, four or more at a time, and since the presence of even small proportions of another metal often serves to modify these phenomena to a profound degree, this task is a truly colossal one and is only being slowly accomplished. At the present time some five or six systems of alloys of two metals have been really thoroughly studied; for the remainder of these relatively simple "binary" alloys we still have to rely upon data which are only rough approximations. Of systems of alloys of three metals only two or three have been closely studied, while systems of four metals are only approached with much difficulty. As it happens, however, the study of the alloys of two metals only has already served to outline most of the fundamental principles which underlie the constitution and structure of all alloys and the changes which they undergo, and these results have proved unexpectedly fruitful in technical practice.

To one class of practical results we have already referred, viz. the power over the properties of the alloys of iron with carbon and with nickel and chromium, which flows from our knowledge of the changes which they undergo when heated to various temperatures and cooled at various rates. Indeed, it is not too much to say that the entire development of modern special "alloy" steels could not have taken place had not the New Metallurgy

## THE TEMPERING OF STEEL 71

directly and indirectly laid the foundation for our knowledge of thermal treatment. Among these developments the modern gun, armour, and armour-piercing shell have already been referred to. Equally important is that very interesting class of materials known as "high speed" tool steels.

Mention has already been made of the fact that tool steel can only be hardened by rapidly cooling or "quenching" it from a temperature above its critical or transformation point. Equally, if hardened steel be heated, then—as the critical temperature is approached—the hardness gradually diminishes and disappears entirely when the critical point is passed. Advantage is, of course, taken of these facts in the ordinary "tempering" of hardened steel, when a tool or blade is gently heated so as to diminish its hardness somewhat in order to gain increased toughness. When, however, a hardened tool is used in a powerful machine, such as a lathe, the point of the tool becomes heated by the violent friction of the metal which it is cutting, and the speed at which the cutting process can be carried on depends entirely upon the fact that the temperature of the point of the tool must not be allowed to rise high enough to bring about the softening of the hardened steel. If this does occur, then the cutting edge immediately breaks down and the tool is spoiled. Now in ordinary carbon tool steels the critical point at which the complete transformation or softening occurs lies in the neighbourhood of 700° C.—a dull red heat; several hundred degrees before this temperature is reached, however, the steel softens so much as to become rapidly useless. Here again we see a series of well-known facts of every-day practice for which the new science finds a theoretical explanation of great scientific interest; and again we find a practical application of the highest importance as the next step. If the existence of the critical point near 700° C. serves to limit the utility of steel cutting tools, cannot that limit of utility be raised by finding some form of steel in which the critical point occurs at a much higher temperature? Fortunately it has been found possible to do this; the addition of either tungsten or molybdenum to steel, together with chromium, produces a whole class of alloy-steels in which the critical temperature is very much higher, and although it is much more difficult to harden these steels—it is necessary to raise them to a white heat (1200° C.) first—yet when once hardened it is not at all easy to soften them again, and tools made of these materials maintain their cutting-power even when worked at such high speeds and pressures that the point of the tool is red-hot and the turnings come away from the lathe visibly "blue" with oxidation owing to the heat generated. The importance of this advance in high-speed machine cutting tools can hardly be over-rated, and there can be no doubt that it is the direct

# ALLOYS

outcome of the New Metallurgy and the flood of light which it has thrown on the meaning and nature of transformations and critical points.

A similar sequence of scientific discoveries and subsequent and entirely unexpected practical advances flowing from them might be developed in several other directions connected with the New Metallurgy—for instance in regard to special steels whose peculiar electrical and magnetic properties serve to lessen to a surprising extent the losses of energy which occur in electrical transformers used in connection with the transmission of power by means of high-tension electric currents. One further example only, however, can be mentioned, and that has been chosen because it serves to illustrate an entirely different direction in which the study of the "constitutional diagram" of a system of alloys may prove to be of surprisingly high practical importance. A study of a number of these diagrams at once brings out the fact that, broadly speaking, there are two distinct types of alloy-systems. In one of these, the two metals unite in much the same way as salt unites with water when it is dissolved in it—a solution is formed when the two metals are melted together and the two do not separate when this solution freezes on cooling. The resulting solid alloy has, in the ideal case, a simple crystalline structure exactly like that of a pure metal, but both metals are present in *each* of the crystals. In the second type of alloys, however, a very different state of affairs is met with; here, although the two metals may still dissolve completely in one another when molten, they crystallise separately on cooling and the resulting solid alloy is a conglomerate of two kinds of crystals. The resulting structures and properties of the two kinds of alloy are, as a result of this diversity in their mode of solidification, very diverse, more particularly when one of the metals of the duplex type of alloy is hard and brittle. There are, however, further complications; in some series of alloys there is no separation of the two component metals when the alloy first solidifies—an aggregate of simple homogeneous crystals is formed; subsequently at some lower temperature—when a critical point is reached—these homogeneous crystals break up and the two constituents separate. This is the change which occurs at the critical point in steel. But even apart from all critical changes, there is another complication which arises when the two metals enter into definite chemical combination with one another; in that case the two kinds of crystal which we find in the resulting alloys are not crystals of the two simple component metals, but crystals of the one metal and crystals of the compound of the two. Now it is a striking fact that these definite intermetallic compounds are peculiarly hard and brittle bodies, even when their component metals are soft and ductile. Thus aluminium and copper—both of which are very

# INTERMETALLIC COMPOUNDS

soft and ductile—form a compound to which the chemical symbol $Al_2Cu$ has been assigned; this consists of long, sharp needle-like crystals which are extremely hard and brittle. If, now, we add copper to aluminium—as is frequently done, with a view to rendering it stronger and harder, the first additions really produce the desired result to a certain extent; the hard crystals of the compound, present as minute particles in the interstices of the softer aluminium crystals, serve to strengthen and stiffen their neighbours, while their soft and ductile surroundings save the brittle crystals of the compound from easy fracture. As soon, however, as the amount of copper is increased and the brittle crystals begin to appear as an important part of the structure, the alloy as a whole also becomes brittle and, therefore, useless for practical purposes. Here we see once again the scientific explanation of facts readily observed and well known in practice. Again, however, we find advance made possible by the utilisation of a further scientific discovery. In this case the discovery in question is that of a system of aluminium alloys in which, although there is not an entire absence of compound formation, yet up to a very considerable limit the first type or class of alloys is followed, so that the two metals solidify in the form of homogeneous crystals without the presence of any distinct brittle constituent. Such a series is found in the alloys of aluminium with zinc, and their utilisation for practical purposes has already produced a series of extremely valuable light alloys of surprising strength. Certain of these possess mechanical properties in regard to strength and ductility equal to those of good mild steel combined with a specific gravity of less than three-eighths that of steel, so that—weight for weight—they are two and one-third times as strong. With the ever-increasing importance of air-craft, and the demand for materials which combine lightness with strength which is thus created, this achievement of modern metallurgy stands out as of first-rate importance. There can be no question that it is a definite fruit of the study of alloys carried out as a scientific study for its own sake.

The examples chosen from the wide field of modern metallurgy briefly outlined above will, it is hoped, be enough to show that in this field the advancement of science—in fact the very growth of a new science—has resulted in industrial developments of the highest possible importance, affecting and in some cases revolutionising what is probably the largest of all the world's industries. It has already been emphasised that to a large extent this new science has grown up as the result of research work carried out with purely scientific purposes. Not only this, but for a long time the exponents of metallurgical practice not merely neglected the young science, but went out of their way to scoff at and to deride it. The remark was sometimes made: "What can the microscopic study of a minute area, no larger than a pin-point,

# THE RESEARCH SPIRIT

tell us about masses of steel weighing fifty tons?" The answer has been found in such matters as those instanced here; that it is now universally admitted is proved by the fact that the methods of the New Metallurgy form part of the regular equipment of every large metallurgical and engineering establishment. The value of the practical results which can be obtained from the New Metallurgy has come to be recognised and the young science has been taken up by the metallurgical industries. It is to be hoped that, none the less, it will be vigorously pursued by its votaries as a pure science for its own sake. In that way alone can we hope for a continuance of the great gifts which it has already bestowed upon us. If the practical spirit—important and valuable as that is in its right place—is permitted to rule our research laboratories, it would be apt to sterilise our investigations and to rob us of the very fruit at which we should be trying to snatch. There is of course—in this as in every branch of science—ample room for what may be termed the "applied" laboratory and the corresponding investigations, whose aim it is to render applicable to definite industrial problems the results already achieved by purely scientific investigation; but over and above these we must—if real progress is to be maintained—keep flowing the pure, bright source of scientific enquiry carried on for its own sake.

# MATHEMATICS IN RELATION TO PURE AND APPLIED SCIENCE

By E. W. HOBSON, F.R.S.

*Sadleirian Professor of Pure Mathematics in the University of Cambridge.*

The part which Mathematics plays at present, and may be expected to play in the future, in the progressive development of Pure and Applied Science, and in the actual applications of scientific methods and knowledge to the work of the world, can be adequately estimated only after some survey of the genesis of Mathematics, and of its historical relations with Physical Science. Accordingly some necessarily brief remarks will here be made on these matters, with a view to a clarification of ideas as to the functions of Mathematics regarded as an indispensable instrument both in the development of the Sciences and in the actual work of applying them to the needs of modern life. The services which Mathematics may be expected to render by co-operation in various departments of Science can be best estimated by considering its past achievements of this sort. It will appear that these services are likely to become of increased importance in many directions, as various sciences reach those more advanced stages in which they present more opportunities than formerly for exact methods of treatment. The consideration of these matters will naturally lead up to some discussion of the educational problems connected with the provision of the necessary outfit of Mathematical knowledge and skill required by those who are to carry out various parts of the mental and practical work of the nation.

Mathematical thought, in a more or less explicit form, pervades every department of human activity. Certain fundamental parts of Mathematics, embodied in the processes and notation of Arithmetic, have become part of the ordinary mental outfit of civilized man. There is perhaps no other branch of science of which this can be asserted with such definiteness. The grocer, when he weighs out his sugar, makes use of Mathematical conceptions which were developed only by a long process of evolution. When he enters his receipts in his books, the notation he employs embodies an invention which, as a mode of economizing labour, must be regarded as one of the triumphs of our race. So simple does our system of numeration seem to us that it requires an effort to realize the fact that the Greeks, with their unsurpassed capacity for abstract thinking, failed to discover it. The navigator, when he uses his logarithmic tables, is utilizing the great invention of John

Napier, the tercentenary of the publication of which was the occasion of a gathering of Mathematicians of all nations a few days before the essential unity of the co-operative work of men of Science was obscured for the immediate future by the outbreak of the European war. The Engineer when he makes the necessary graphical calculations of the stresses in the bridge he is building, or the Statistician who constructs his graphs, has to employ methods and conceptions belonging to a relatively advanced state of mathematical thought. The Philosopher, in his reflections on spatial and temporal relations, on number and quantity, on matter and motion, is in a region in which the boundary between his own domain and that of the Mathematician is scarcely discernible. By the Epistemologist mathematical knowledge has always been taken as a kind of touchstone on which to test his general theories of the nature of knowledge.

The origins of Mathematical thinking, and the reason of its ubiquity in all departments of Science that have reached a certain maturity, and even in practical life, are not far to seek. The physical world which forms our environment appears to us as a manifold of objects extended in space, the spatial relations of the various objects exhibiting at any one time an endless variety, and varying at different times. The primary mathematical operations of counting and measuring, which give rise in the reflecting mind to the concepts of number

# EVOLUTION OF MATHEMATICAL CONCEPTS

and geometric form, took their first beginnings in the practical interests of man living in the physical world. Those mathematical concepts, and the methods of dealing with them systematically, underwent a gradual evolution in close connection with the practical efforts required to grasp, classify and characterize, and so far as possible to dominate, the spatial relations of actual bodies, both in their fixity and as changing in temporal succession. The more closely men scrutinized the external world, at first for practical reasons, and later from intellectual curiosity as well, the more things and processes they found to have aspects which are measurable, and the more frequently they were able to employ their nascent mathematical processes and concepts for the precise characterization of physical objects and phenomena. However abstract, and remote from their origins in sensuous experience, great branches of Mathematics have become in modern times, they all have their roots in the primitive intuitions of time, space, and matter. Mathematics was then in its beginnings essentially a Physical Science, distinguished from other special branches of Science mainly by the fact that the universality and relative simplicity of those aspects of the world with which Mathematics was primarily concerned facilitated a comparatively rapid process of schematization by abstraction. An effect of such schematization was the gradual evolution of an elaborate symbolism which, in modern times, has given great prominence to the formal aspect of the subject and to a technique requiring effort and aptitude for its acquirement to any considerable degree of success. In other branches of Science the disentanglement of the relevant aspects of the phenomena concerned is a process of greater complexity than in the case of Mathematics, and consequently the process of reduction to a schematic form is in every case in a much less advanced stage. Some branches have as yet advanced but little beyond the purely classificatory stage. It is a matter for speculation how far the various branches of Science may be expected to proceed along the same path as in the case of Mathematics, the end of which is a purely rationalized representation of the phenomena concerned in a schematic form. One of our most prominent Biologists has been heard to assert, at a scientific gathering, that the ultimate goal of Biological Science consists in its reduction to Pure Mathematics. The case of Geometry affords the most striking example of a science reduced to the purely deductive stage; originally developed by induction from spatial observations it has no longer need to have recourse to observation for its further development. It may be regarded as the type towards which each department of science tends to conform as it becomes more rationalized, that is as it becomes less dependent at every point on purely empirical elements. Completely rationalized Physics and Chemistry

# PHYSICS AND MATHEMATICS 83

would contain within themselves, in the form of postulates, every element which could be supplied by physical observation, and would no longer be dependent for their future progress upon the work of the experimenter. Laboratories would then be useful only for illustrative, didactic, and suggestive purposes, just as drawings and models are still used in Geometry, but they would no longer hold their present indispensable position in relation to research. The progress of these sciences would, as in the case of Geometry at present, consist in a detailed development of the schematic representations of the phenomena. The actual state of these departments of Science is of course vastly different from the ideal state to which reference has been made, but there exist in almost all departments of science coherent tracts within which mathematical methods become applicable. In the course of advance in each department, as it reaches the stages in which it is possible to come to closer grips with the phenomena under examination, there arise increasing demands for the application of mathematical methods and reasoning, sometimes of course of only an elementary kind, but often later on of a more advanced character.

The connection of Physics, cosmical and terrestrial, with Mathematics is so close that all parts of the subject are accessible in greater or less degree to mathematical treatment. The part of Physics which was developed earliest, the Mechanics of solid and fluid bodies in the gross, has been from the beginning in such close contact with Mathematics that theoretical mechanics has always been regarded as an integral part of Mathematics. This arose from the fact that the phenomena involved are of such a character that they lend themselves easily to measurement, and comparatively easily to the formulation of laws expressible in precise terms. Mechanics may then be regarded as a science that is rationalized in a degree only less complete than is the case in the model instance of Geometry. In those parts of Physics such as Sound, Light, Heat, and Elasticity, in which the subtler properties of matter are involved, the line of progress has consisted largely of reduction, with ever increasing success, to dynamical treatment, in which the detailed representation of the phenomena is sought in the extension of Mechanics to the smallest parts of matter, or as in the case of light, to the parts of a hypothetical medium in which the light is regarded as being propagated. The application of ever more refined mathematical methods to the determination and tabulation of the motion of the heavenly bodies has proceeded rapidly in our own time and has as yet by no means reached its zenith. The foundation on a dynamical basis of the Science of Celestial Mechanics by Newton has been regarded as probably the greatest and most far reaching contribution to the advance of Science ever made in our country.

# DYNAMICAL THEORY OF TIDES

There are many cases in which the phenomena to be investigated are complicated by so many details of local or other circumstances that they do not lend themselves to immediate treatment by pure theory without the admixture of a large amount of purely empirical data. In such cases results of great value have often been obtained by a mixed method, partly dynamical, and partly empirical; this is frequently the case when a purely mathematical analysis of the phenomena concerned is beyond the present powers of mathematicians. A striking instance of such mixed method is afforded by the case of the calculation of tables predicting the tides at a particular port. In accordance with the dynamical theory of the tides regarded as due to the disturbing effect of the attraction of the moon and sun on the water the actual height of the tide at a given time has been shown to be due to the superimposition of a number of simple tides each of which has a definite period. One of these simple tides, the chief one in most parts of the world, has a period of half a day, another has a period of a whole day, and there are others of various periods dependent on the month and the year. A considerable number of these simple tides, the period of each of which has been obtained by the mathematical theory, must be taken account of; but though the period of each of these is thus given by theory the maximum height of each is not so ascertainable, because it depends on a vast variety of special circumstances, such as the conformation of the land and the shape of the basin of the sea. Accordingly the problem of determining the height of the tide at a given future time is resolved by making a very considerable number of observations of the tide at the particular port, and utilizing the results of such observations to determine the maxima of the simple tides of known periods of which the actual tide is made up. This process is actually carried out by a machine devised for the purpose, and thus a table available for future times can be calculated on the basis of this combination of theory with observation. Other examples of this mixed method are being applied in the processes adopted for the calculation of the trajectories of projectiles, and in problems connected with air-craft, especially in relation to the very important questions as to the stability of machines of various types. In recent years mathematical methods have been applied with increasing frequency to the statistical analysis of large masses of measurable observations of some prescribed type, in cases in which no dynamical or other theory as to the cause of the phenomena in question is assumed *a priori*. The statistical method has been largely applied in biological science by a school of investigators to obtain information as to the correlation of different determining factors. Although there is at present much difference of

# MATHEMATICS AND PHYSICAL SCIENCE

opinion as to the precise scope and conditions of validity of the processes adopted by Biometricians, it is practically certain that their methods will, in some degree, form a permanent part of the stock of implements employed by biological investigators. In Economic Science also mathematical methods have recently attained to a considerable and increasing prominence.

It is a very common misconception to suppose that the sole function of Mathematics in relation to various departments of Physical Science is that of providing the means of carrying out whatever calculations may be necessary; and thus that Mathematics plays in these sciences a comparatively humble part analogous to that of a mechanical tool. As a matter of fact mathematical thinking has done very much more than merely to provide methods of calculating; it has often played a dominant part in the formation of the concepts with which the Physical Sciences work; it has decided in many cases for them not only how to calculate but what the things are that they ought to calculate; it has reduced the originally vague conceptions which arise in connection with physical observation to precise forms in which they can be exhibited as measurable quantities. Some of these concepts could only have been definitely formulated as the result of a long train of previous mathematical development. For example, the conception of Energy as a measurable quantity, and the exact meaning of the great generalization known to us as the law of the Conservation of Energy, emerged as results of the development of the abstract side of molar Mechanics, which determined the modes in which the kinetic energy of moving bodies and potential energy as work are defined as measurable quantities. Only by the transference and extension of these notions to the molecular domain did the formulation of the modern doctrine become possible. The doctrine of the conservation of energy for the case of molar bodies had been established before Joule and Mayer commenced their work, and was a necessary presupposition of this further development. Joule was able to determine the mechanical equivalent of heat only owing to the fact that mechanical work was already regarded as a measurable quantity, measured in a manner which had been fixed in the course of the establishment of the older Mathematical Mechanics. The notion of Potential, fundamental in Electrical Science, upon which the units employed by the Electrical Engineer depend, was first developed as a mathematical conception during the eighteenth century in connection with the theory of the attractions of gravitating bodies. It was transferred to the electrical domain by George Green and others, together with a good deal of detailed mathematics connected with it which had previously been applied to the gravitational potential function.

The man of true Physical instincts, endowed

## OPTICS AND MATHEMATICS

with that faculty of scientific imagination, which was possessed for example by Lord Kelvin in a superlative degree, is for ever imagining models which shall enable him by their working to represent and depict the course of actual physical processes. The possibility and consistency of such models require Mathematical Analysis for their investigation. The mathematician may also, by tracing the necessary consequences of the postulation of a model of a particular type, formulate crucial tests in accordance with which further experiments will decide whether a particular type of model can be retained, at least provisionally, or whether it must be rejected as inadequate for the representation of the known facts, and must give place to some other model of a different type. Perhaps the most striking example of the services which have been rendered to Science by the contemplation of various models, many or all of which have ultimately been found to be inadequate for complete representation, is to be found in the history of Optics. The various forms of the corpuscular theory, and of the wave theory, of Light were all attempts to represent the phenomena by models, the value of which had to be estimated by developing their mathematical consequences, and by comparing these consequences with the results of experiments. The adynamical theory of Fresnel, the elastic solid theory of the ether developed by Navier, Cauchy, Poisson, and Green, the labile ether theory developed by Cauchy and Kelvin, and the rotational ether theory of Mac-Cullagh were all efforts of the kind here indicated; they were all successful in some greater or less degree in the representation of the phenomena, and they all stimulated Physicists to further efforts to obtain more minute knowledge of those phenomena. Even such an inadequate theory as that of Fresnel led to the very interesting observation by Humphry Lloyd of the phenomenon of conical refraction in crystals, as the result of the prediction by W. Rowan Hamilton that the phenomenon was a necessary consequence of the mathematical fact that Fresnel's wave surface in a biaxal crystal possesses four conical points.

In the history of Science it is possible to find cases in which the tendency of Mathematics to express itself in forms of ever increasing degrees of abstractness has proved to be of ultimate service in the physical order of ideas. Perhaps the most striking example is to be found in the development of abstract Dynamics. The greatest treatise on this subject which the world has seen is Lagrange's *Mécanique Analytique* published in 1788. The spirit in which this great work was conceived is best described in the Preface. Lagrange writes: "We have already various treatises on Mechanics, but the plan of this one is entirely new. I intend to reduce the theory of this Science, and the art of solving problems relating to it, to general

## ABSTRACT DYNAMICS

formulae, the simple development of which provides all the equations necessary for the solution of each problem." "No diagrams will be found in this work. The methods that I explain require neither geometrical, nor mechanical, constructions or reasoning, but only algebraical operations in accordance with regular and uniform procedure. Those who love Analysis will see with pleasure that Mechanics has become a branch of it, and will be grateful to me for having thus extended its domain." If ever a work was conceived in the purely abstract mathematical spirit it is surely this one. It is very interesting to trace its effects. Lagrange's idea of reducing the investigation of the motion of a dynamical system to a form dependent upon a single function of the generalized co-ordinates and velocities of the system was further developed by Hamilton and Jacobi into forms in which the equations of motion of the system represent the conditions for a stationary value of an integral of a single function. The extension by Routh and Helmholtz to the case in which "ignored co-ordinates" are taken into account, was a step in the desirable unification which would be attained if the notion of potential energy were removed by interpreting it as dependent upon the kinetic energy of concealed motions included in the dynamical system. The whole scheme of abstract Dynamics' thus developed upon the basis of Lagrange's work has been of immense value in Physics, and particularly in statistical Mechanics, which is now a subject of great importance. But the most striking use of Lagrange's conception of generalized co-ordinates was made by Clerk Maxwell who, in this order of ideas, conceived and developed his dynamical theory of the Electromagnetic field, and obtained his celebrated equations. This great achievement was rendered possible by the fact that the use of generalized co-ordinates enables the dynamical equations of a system to be set up in cases in which the detailed structure of the system is in part unknown. The form of Maxwell's equations enabled him to perceive that oscillations could be propagated in the electromagnetic field with the velocity of light, and suggested to him the electromagnetic theory of light. Heinrich Herz, under the direct inspiration of Maxwell's ideas, demonstrated the possibility of setting up electromagnetic waves which differ from those of light only in respect of their enormously greater length. We thus see that Lagrange's work, conceived in the spirit he has himself described, was an essential link in a chain of investigation which led, on the practical side, to the invention of wireless telegraphy.

Mathematics has also, at various times, exercised a potent influence upon general thought. The revolutionary effect of the modern Mathematical Astronomy, inaugurated by Copernicus, due to the change in our notions of the relative position of the Earth in the solar system and in the stellar universe,

# GEOMETRY

is well known. A much more recent example of modification of philosophic thought, as the result of mathematical research, will here be referred to, viz. the effect of modern theories of Geometry upon our conceptions of spatial relations.

The properties and relations assigned to the ideal objects of rational Geometry were suggested by observations of spatial relations in the physical world; there are however noteworthy limitations to the amount of leading that can in this regard be obtained from our actual perceptions. In the first place, all our spatial perceptions are affected by an essential element of inexactitude, the amount of which varies with the degree of precision of the instruments we use for measurement, but which can never be wholly eliminated. In the second place, all our actual observations have reference to some more or less bounded, and certainly finite, portion of what we call physical space, although we have the intuition that it is always possible to pass beyond the space at any time observed. In rational Geometry, we have in the scheme of axioms, definitions, and postulates, not only to make precise statements as to the possession of certain entities of certain precise properties, whereas the corresponding physical objects possess those properties only roughly, but we have also to make statements which refer to what happens in every part of unbounded space; and to do this we have to pass in certain respects beyond anything we can learn from physical observation. In one point, namely in connection with what is usually known as the axiom of parallels, this disability has proved to be of the greatest importance in the development of the Science. Euclid's axiom of parallels, being a statement of what happens in unbounded space, is essentially incapable of direct verification. Indirect verification, for example, by observation of the sum of the angles of a triangle, is indecisive, on account of the essential inexactitude of our measurements, and on account of the fact that the size of the triangles that can be observed, even by the Astronomer, is limited. All the numerous attempts that have been made to prove the truth of the axiom, that is to show that it is logically deducible from the other axioms and postulates, proved a failure in face of the most determined efforts to throw light upon the matter; it has now been demonstrated that this failure was inevitable. It is absolutely necessary for the development of rational geometry, either to postulate, as Euclid does, in some form or other, the truth of the axiom of parallels, or else to substitute for it some postulate of a divergent character, but still not inconsistent with our intuitions of actual spatial relations. During the last century, the actual failure to prove the truth of Euclid's axiom within the rational scheme, led to the investigation of the results of making a different postulation, and at least two systems, that of Bolyai-Lobachewsky,

## GEOMETRY

and that of Riemann, were invented. Each of these contains a substitute for Euclid's axiom, and is inconsistent with it, and they are inconsistent with one another; but each is, when suitably interpreted, a sufficient representation of our actual spatial perceptions, although not so simple a representative scheme as that of Euclid. It has been demonstrated that each of these schemes is logically self-consistent, and thus the possibility of diverging conceptual schemes for the representation of a single set of perceptual data has in this instance been established. This is a result of great general interest. The view is no longer tenable that the relations of space and time exist in the mind as empty forms of thought, as in Kant's scheme, prior to all ·perception; as forms in which all our spatial and temporal perceptions clothe themselves. Nor is it true that the conceptual schemes for spatial relations are simple products of empirical observation. They could never have arisen apart from our actual experience of the external world, but they contain more than the raw data obtained from perception. The rise from the rough data of sensuous perception to a rational scheme representing the relations concerned can only be accomplished by a process in which the reflective activities of the mind, co-operating with sensuous perception, contribute an essential element which is lacking in the data themselves. It is a very important fact, fully established by the recent history of Geometry, that the mode in which the data of the senses can be idealized and completed leaves a latitude in which there is a considerable element of free choice left to the mind. This element of free choice has been exercised in the construction of various types of Geometry, all of which are logically possible, *i.e.* self-consistent, and several of which are equally applicable for the representation of our actual spatial experience. This remarkable result suggests that in other sciences it is possible that the system of laws forming the schematic representation of the phenomena may not necessarily be unique; that there may be in any given domain several, or an unlimited number, of different possible schemes which will all be equally valid; although, as in the case of Geometry, they will not be all equally simple.

The sketch which has been given above of the influence of Mathematics in other departments of thought and work, has necessarily confined itself in the main to a few specially striking examples. Indeed it is practically certain that the number and scope of the applications of Mathematical methods both in the development of pure Science, and in Engineering and other technical pursuits, will largely increase in the not distant future. As each branch of science reaches a stage of greater maturity, and as each kind of technical work becomes more open to scientific treatment, new opportunities will arise for the application of Mathematics. It is clearly essential for an adequate fulfilment of these demands upon Mathematical Science that the requisite knowledge and skill should be forthcoming in ample measure. Accordingly, in the consideration of the means of increasing national efficiency, so far as it depends upon scientific training, questions relating to mathematical education and research must receive a considerable share of attention. The essential requisites as regards Mathematics are much the same as in other branches of knowledge. They consist in a thoroughly well thought out system of instruction, graduated according to the needs of various classes of students, in the training of a competent body of teachers of every grade, and in the encouragement of mathematical research in the Universities and other higher educational establishments.

Many reforms have been introduced of late years in the school teaching of Mathematics. The powerful influence of the Mathematical Association, which has focussed and sifted the views of the most thoughtful and observant of the teachers of the subject, has contributed much to the introduction of improved methods of teaching; and the Universities have also effected something by means of changes in the syllabuses of their more elementary examinations. The older traditional teaching of Mathematics in schools, by its undue insistence upon the purely abstract side of the subject, was apt to produce upon the pupil the impression that Mathematics was an arid subject out of relation with everything outside itself. The repulsive effect upon most minds produced by a subject so presented is held to be the chief explanation of the low standard of the knowledge attained by a large proportion of the pupils. The newer kind of teaching is based upon the idea that the interest of the pupil should be stimulated at every point by directing his attention to actual or possible applications of what is being learned; in fact by showing him that Mathematics is really connected with certain aspects of the actual world, and is an instrument which can be employed for a variety of practical ends. The newer methods based upon a wider view of the functions of the teaching, and upon a more enlightened apprehension of the Psychology of the immature mind, have their characteristic dangers when pushed too far, and have in fact led to a certain amount of reaction in favour of the older methods. It is certain that the newer methods of teaching make incomparably greater demands than the older methods upon the skill and alertness of mind of the teacher. It is probably true that the results obtained by an incompetent teacher, who attempts the reformed methods, may in some respects even fall short of those he might have obtained under the older system.

The disestablishment of Euclid's Elements of Geometry which, until some years ago, had the unique position of holding a practical monopoly as a scientific text book, has given an opportunity for carrying out experiments in methods of teaching the very important subject of Geometry. The view that the study of Geometry, in its earliest stages, should be of a practical kind, appealing to sensuous intuition and observation, has met with very general acceptance. There is however much difference of opinion as to the relations between the practical and the abstract treatment of the subject in the later stages. By the advocates of the use of Euclid or of some other text book on more or less similar lines great stress is laid upon the importance of the study of Geometry as affording a training in logical thinking of the deductive kind. Those who lay most weight upon the practical side of the subject regard a detailed knowledge of spatial relations as the chief object to be attained. The greater part of the actual teaching of the subject is very properly based upon a compromise between the two extreme views of the objects to be attained. There is evidence that the purely practical treatment of the subject has been carried to an unfortunate extreme by some teachers; and this has naturally led in some quarters to a strong reaction in favour of more rigorous methods. That the most effective methods of teaching the subject must provide for both the logical and the intuitional treatment of spatial relations is quite clear; although there will no doubt continue to be differences of opinion amongst teachers as to the proportions in which these two elements should be combined. There has been some expression of opinion in favour of again stereotyping the subject by means of the imposition of a single authorized text book; but although the carrying out of such a proposal would undoubtedly be a convenience for the examiner, it is to be deprecated in the interest of the freedom of the teacher. Even if the accuracy of the results of examination were thereby increased, it would be a very insufficient reason for fettering the teacher; for one of the most serious evils from which our educational system has suffered has been the subordination of the freedom of the teaching to the exigencies of examinations. Although we now possess schemes of Geometry in which, by the placing of all the intuitional elements at the beginning, in the form of postulates and definitions, the subsequent treatment is made purely deductive, it will be recognized by all who are acquainted with the nature, number, and complication of these postulates and definitions, that such treatment of the subject is quite unsuitable for use except by specialists in an advanced stage of their course. That Euclid's Elements of Geometry embodied a purely logical treatment of the subject, of unimpeachable rigour, is far from being true. At numerous points in the course of his reasoning, Euclid has recourse to unproved and unstated

# THE TEACHING OF MECHANICS

assumptions, the truth of which is intuitional, but does not follow from his scheme of axioms and postulates.

Of late years much has been done to check the undue expenditure of time and energy, in the customary treatment of Algebra, upon the acquirement of skill in the manipulation of artificially complicated algebraical expressions. Indeed no subject has suffered more from its own technique than Algebra; much effort which should have been directed towards the acquirement of really fruitful ideas has been wasted upon an often vain effort to acquire an almost mechanical dexterity in dealing with symbols out of relation with the concrete. The time gained by the restriction of this kind of work to the necessary minimum has, in the hands of the best teachers, been employed, to the lasting advantage of the pupils, in giving them some comprehension of the use of the subject in dealing with actualities, and in extending their mental vision by means of an appropriately simple introduction to the principles of the Calculus.

Both in Schools and Universities the teaching of Mechanics has suffered from the undue separation of the Mathematical and the Experimental teaching of the subject. Neither treatment of the subject can be satisfactory without at least some admixture of the other. Although, in a teaching course, the precise relation between the two sides of the subject must largely depend upon the ultimate aims of the students, it is certain that either an exclusive fixing of the attention upon the abstract side of the subject, or a merely qualitative observation of phenomena of motion and rest without a precise study of their quantitative aspect, will very materially diminish the advantages derived from this fundamentally important study.

The mode in which mathematical teaching should be adapted to the needs of students of Engineering Science has received much attention during the last two decades. That much of the mathematical teaching current in the Universities and other institutions was too purely abstract in character, and that too much time was spent on an accumulated mass of details which obscured the principles of the subject, to be suitable for students whose primary aim was to learn how to apply Mathematics, has been very generally admitted. The recognition of this has led to the setting up of special courses of instruction and to the production of numerous text books intended to meet the needs of such students. Although undoubtedly much good work has been accomplished in this direction there is distinct danger of an excess in that revulsion against pure theory which is exhibited in some of the current treatment of what is known as practical Mathematics. It cannot be too strongly insisted upon that a firm grasp of principles, as distinct from the mere processes of calculation, is essential, if Mathematics is to be a tool really useful to the engineer. There is a real danger that such students may learn to regard Mathematics as consisting merely of formulae and rules which provide the means of performing the numerical computations necessary for solving certain kinds of problems which occur in the practical sciences. Apart from the deplorable effect, on the educational side, of degrading Mathematics to this level, the practical effect of reducing it to a number of rule-of-thumb processes can only be to make those who learn it in so unintelligent a manner incapable of applying mathematical methods to any practical problem in which the data differ even slightly from those in the model problems which they have studied. Mathematics cannot be effectively studied in a frame of mind in which impatience is excited whenever the application to practical problems of what is learned is not immediately obvious. The mathematical instruction of students of Engineering is likely to be more efficient when it is imparted by a mathematician who has acquired a sympathetic comprehension of the points of view and of the needs of such students than if it is in the hands of an engineer who regards Mathematics merely as a subsidiary subject.

Many important questions connected with the teaching of the more advanced parts of mathematics in our Universities must here be left aside. In the older Universities at least, fewer students than formerly are prepared to spend the whole time during their course upon the study of the subject; but this change has been more than compensated for by the large increase in the number of those who, after spending part of their time on Mathematics, proceed to the study of the Physical or Engineering Sciences or to other studies. There is good hope that this tendency to combine the study of Mathematics with that of other subjects in which the training and skill so obtained may be made available will go considerably further than at present. The divorce in many places prevalent between mathematical and physical studies has been productive of much injury to the mental development and ultimate efficiency of many of our students.

In order that our country may contribute its due share to the advance of Science, and that a progressive spirit may be maintained in the ranks of those engaged in the teaching of Mathematics, it is essential that ample provision for Mathematical Research be made in the Universities and other higher institutions where scientific studies are pursued. To this end there must exist in all such places a sufficient number of posts in which the teaching work expected from the holders is sufficiently restricted to leave ample leisure for independent work. The mathematical research to be thus encouraged should be various in kind, ranging from abstract Pure Mathematics, through

Mathematical Physics, to the constructive work of applying mathematical methods to various species of practical problems. As in other branches of science, the most far-reaching discoveries in mathematics have been made for the most part by persons whose primary interests were in the subject itself, and not in the applications outside. Any attempt to discourage perfectly untrammelled research in those parts of the subject that are most remote from practical interests, or that show least promise of fruitful application in other branches of science, would not only be a vital blow to Mathematics as an ever growing Science, but would ultimately impair its efficiency as an instrument. Mathematics can only flourish if it has full autonomy. The nature and direction of its future applications in pure and applied science can never be fully foreseen. It is however extremely probable that the services it will render in the future will cover an even greater range than in the past, provided it is allowed to fit itself for rendering such services by according it full opportunity to develop itself in accordance with its own nature.

# THE SCIENCE OF BOTANY AND THE ART OF INTENSIVE CULTIVATION

By F. W KEEBLE, F.R.S.

*Director of the Royal Horticultural Society's Gardens, Wisley.*

The task that is laid upon the contributors to these pages is no light one. Two years ago most of us were engrossed in our professional duty of endeavouring to enlarge the boundaries of natural knowledge. Absorbed in this exacting labour our daily life was led somewhat apart from that of the great body of the nation. Each of us worked on a narrow front, engaged upon a special task, somewhat oblivious of the others' labours and inclined to be indifferent to the nation's immediate needs and problems. At heart we were no doubt not ungrateful for the leisure and opportunity with which the State provided us for the pursuit of our several studies; but generally prone in our excursions into the larger world to affect a tone of superiority, to lecture our fellow men on their neglect of science and to deplore the small part which scientific method plays in the government of the State.

As the result of our collective work and in spite of many individual failures, scientific discovery advanced its slow conquest of knowledge. We worked in friendly co-operation with our fellow men of science in other countries and rendered unto the Teutonic Caesar the things that were Caesar's—and some that were not. We preached now and then a sermon on aniline dyes to deaf ears; but on the whole we were content with the somewhat inefficient government and administration which we enjoyed. We jested lightly on the subject of our foreign consuls and their general detachment from commercial affairs and we rather deplored the misfortune that men trained in the classics and the art of litigation were set in authority over us. We gave no heed to the fiction beloved of statesmen and other managers of men that their high work is beyond the powers of mere thinkers and men of science, and by our general remoteness and aversion from affairs we appeared to accept this naive judgment by default. So we continued—and to the State " grew stranger being ...rapt in secret studies." Then the war cloud appeared on the horizon and whilst we smiled at the absurdity of such an anachronism as an European conflict, it burst overwhelmingly upon us. As the best of the young men of all other classes flocked to the recruiting stations so the best of our youth left microscope and test tube and galvanometer on the laboratory bench and went out and fought and died for England. A few "sicklied o'er with the pale cast of thought" discovered conscientious objections to fighting themselves; though conscience did not in all cases prevent them from continuing to accept the favours of the State, receive its emoluments, and enjoy the security purchased by the sword they could not wield. Others of our number were pressed into the service of the State, to aid in the organisation of the forces and resources of the Crown. Although the details of the work which they have done may not yet be published, sufficient is known to demonstrate to all the world what we knew beforehand, that British men of science are not inferior to the Germans in either knowledge or resourcefulness.

Though many were taken for war work some of us were left. That was inevitable. As well might sundry molecules complain in the days when chaos was in process of conversion into order that they had been left unemployed until the seventh day. After the sharp disappointment proper to patriotism and inevitable to the vanity of man we realise to-day that there is work for us to do: that appertaining to the peace of the seventh day. We are learning that the part we are called upon to play is to exercise not only fortitude for the present but also prevision for the future. This duty is of course by no means exclusively or specially ours. It devolves on all men in like case with us, and it is the duty of the men of British birth who cannot be engaged in seeking peace through victory on the field so to prepare that when peace comes it may be the herald of a new and better era in the annals of the Empire and of civilisation. Not by contentiousness but in a spirit of conciliation may we contribute our share to this work. If the several classes of the nation fail in this task of reconstruction it will not be for lack of intelligence but for lack of good temper. The British are a fair-minded race, tenacious alike of their rights and privileges and of their prepossessions. We prize the defects of our virtue of liberty as dearly as the virtue itself. We can never conform with the Prussian idea of a State founded on the polity of the ants and the bees and the wasps. Our instinct tells us that German efficiency has been purchased at too high a price, and our instinct is right; albeit our habitual neglect to make any but grudgingly small outlays on the commodity may, if we persist in the parsimony, prove our undoing.

Expressed in its largest terms the national duty consists in conserving the instinct of liberty whilst developing the habit of obedience. The one is our system of national insurance, the other the means of national prosperity. By the exercise of the habit we may gain the whole world; but by the loss of the instinct we lose our own soul.

We claim not without reason to understand the art of compromise. Now is the supreme moment when we must put that art into practice. Misery makes strange bedfellows, and in our present peril —peril of ourselves less than peril of a slave State such as Germany—liberty, taught consideration, and discipline, dignified by intelligence, must learn to run in double harness. In our own sphere we might well make a beginning by calling a friendly truce between the big-endians and little-endians of Classics and Science. For if the protagonists were to confer instead of to contend they would discover that in the ample years of leisure which our youth enjoy there is room in plenty for both classical and scientific education. In such a spirit of sweet reasonableness the scientific and the classico-clerical might proceed together to a reform of our system of education—from top to bottom. There is room for it. It is essential that our statesmen and administrators, our teachers and our poets know something of the work and method and beauty of science. It is no less essential that the men of science of the coming generation should be cultivated citizens as well as competent specialists.

It is not, however, the purpose of this volume, as I conceive it, to give occasion to sundry men of science to lament at large; but rather, each in his proper sphere, to review the special subject which on this occasion he is privileged to represent and to endeavour to discover and suggest means whereby it may be rendered of greater service both to the State and to the human race.

Inasmuch as, according to the conservative estimate of Locke, half the quarrels of mankind are quarrels about words, it is necessary to define the terms which our several tasks compel us to employ. In the present case it is the more necessary in that the title of this essay "The Science of Botany and the Art of Intensive Cultivation," seems to suggest a sharp antithesis between what are known as pure and applied science. There is no such antithesis. Pure and applied science differ not in method but in aim. Pure science pursues knowledge in order to minister to the general and ultimate wants of mankind; applied science pursues it in order to minister to the special and immediate wants of mankind. They both observe the same rules of the chase; both hunt the same forest. The only difference between them is that whereas pure science seeks ever to pursue its hunting in regions wherein no trapper has set foot, applied science awaits with gun and snare the quarry driven by pure science.

But if the beaters are few or inexpert and fail to rouse all the game of the forest the guns must do their own beating. Then will the bag be leaner. Although it is the function of pure science to pursue knowledge without regard to the industrial or social uses to which the knowledge it seeks may be put, it is under no prohibition to restrict its activities. Pure science is not required to make statutory declaration beforehand that no one will be a penny the richer if it succeed. There are times and the present is such a time when pure science does well to renew its touch with national life; and this no less for its own sake than for the sake of the nation. There would seem to be no sanction for the opinion not infrequently expressed that *all* the knowledge which science accumulates is worth having: that though useless for the welfare of mankind it is and must be useful to the mind of man. Apart altogether from its social or commercial utility scientific work, like any work of art, may be of a good or bad, of a valuable or useless kind: a means of access to new domains of knowledge or a blind alley leading nowhere. The premisses and unproven assumptions on which a piece of scientific work may rest are so numerous and so fallible that although the facts ascertained in the course of the enquiry may themselves be true, the enquiry may advance knowledge not at all. For facts to be of service to science must be discovered at the right time and in the right relationship one to the other.

It follows therefore if these statements be true that not all the kinds of investigation fashionable at a given epoch are necessarily of worth. And, if this be true, it also follows that it behoves the leaders in a particular science to confer with one another in order to ascertain whether the bias they are giving to aspirants to research is never in the direction of one of these scientific culs de sac. Thirty years ago it may have been legitimate to aspire to elucidate the course of evolution by detailed and minute comparison of the morphology of plants. We know to-day that the aspiration will not be realised in this manner. Again some critics might urge that historical research into the priority of rival specific names is absorbing but is not science; that it is merely an elegant accomplishment like the Italian handwriting and the ready swooning habit of the ladies of an earlier century. Though some might maintain that all the elaborate work on the demarcation of the germ-layers of plants has resulted in a permanent enrichment of science others would be found to hold that the work led nowhither and must all be done again in the style in which zoologists are doing it and with the object of defining the parental contributions to the dual individual.

It is not with the object of exciting controversy that these illustrations are put forward; but rather to draw attention to the need for a conference between botanists on the present trend of the science. In the mean time we might all read a little of Voltaire as a corrective to the optimism of Pope.

The function of pure science is to pursue *useful* knowledge; the duty of the leaders of science is to direct the pursuit along what appear to them the most promising lines. It is no less their duty to recognise that it becomes necessary from time to time to call off the hounds of science and to try a fresh scent.

Nor will they forget that by useful knowledge is meant knowledge which contributes to the moral, social, intellectual, aesthetic, and material welfare of mankind.

The need for the review and co-ordination of botanical work is now at its greatest. As the Republic discovered not so long after it had cut off Lavoisier's head, the State *has* need of savants—of botanists among others. Thus, if it is to carry out successfully its rural programme with the inevitable fiscal changes of policy, if it is to repopulate the country side, to clothe once again the hills with forests, to replace poor grass by corn—in short to colonise Great Britain and Ireland, the State must have our enthusiastic co-operation as well as that of other and more socially important sections of the community. There is no need either to emphasise the importance of this problem of home colonisation nor to declare that it is one the solution of which will demand the co-operation of all classes of the commonwealth. In this joint enterprise there is a definite work in which Botanists are competent to co-operate. That work concerns the intensive cultivation of the land. To this it may be objected—with a certain measure of

## SCIENCE OF INTENSIVE CULTIVATION

truth—that botanists are more concerned with dead than with living plants: that many of us could prescribe a variety of recipes for the elegant killing of plants but few would be able to keep them decently alive.

Needless to say the suggestion that botanists should concentrate their attention on problems of intensive cultivation does not mean that they should usurp the function of gardeners and farmers. It means that in the national interest no less than in the interest of Botany they should devote all the attention possible to the pure science of intensive cultivation. They no less than the workers in scientific agriculture and horticulture must help to bridge the gulf between the laboratory and the land. It will of course—and more seriously—be objected that the intensive cultivation of the land is in part a craft and in part an applied science. Very well, then, give the workers in applied science the pure science they must employ. It cannot be insisted on too strongly that the assumption which underlies the segregation of science into pure and applied is by no means wholly valid. According to that assumption, pure science discovers and formulates general principles or laws and applied science makes practical application of these laws to particular cases in order to secure utilitarian ends. But the distinction between these two divisions of science can rarely be maintained. Was Metchnikoff's work on inflammation and the rôle of phagocytes therein pure or applied science? When Pasteur gave the Lilleois pure beer he made a notable contribution to the well-being of the race,—"For malt does more than Milton can To justify God's ways to man,"—but by the same research he fathomed the nature of fermentation and laid a corner stone in the foundation of preventive medicine. Now at this present time the country has need and urgent need of a greater knowledge of the laws which govern the productivity of plants. These laws it is within the competence of botanists to investigate. Why should we not concentrate our efforts upon the discovery of these laws and thereby seek at one and the same time to advance our science and to assist the workers in the applied sciences of agriculture and horticulture? It is true that, thanks to the provisions made by the Development Commissioners and by the Board of Agriculture, Institutes have been established for the purpose of investigating the problems of intensive cultivation. But in the dearth of knowledge of general laws or principles these Institutes have to combine the work of applied with that of pure science. They have first to grow their own straw before they can make the bricks.

Yet the briefest review of recent progress in methods of intensive cultivation discloses the fact that it is the Paul of pure Science that has planted and the Apollos of applied science that has watered the germs of discovery to which this progress is due.

In older days the problem of intensive cultivation appeared to be relatively simple. It was stated by Swift in the famous aphorism of the two blades of grass. Now it is recognised that the problem is exceedingly complex. The text of the aphorism must be extended. Not only must two "blades" be grown in lieu of one, not only must the crop be larger, it must also be of better quality, more resistant to disease, ripe at a suitable time, produced at the greatest possible net profit without undue impoverishment of the land. The problem of intensive cultivation is thus seen to involve both scientific and economic considerations. To solve it crop and soil and population, market and labour, housing and fiscal policy must all be taken into consideration. It would be an invaluable piece of work if the Development Commissions or some other competent authority were to draw up and publish an authoritative statement of the ends and means of intensive cultivation; for at present the problem is envisaged piecemeal. To attempt such a task is beyond both the scope of this essay and the competence of the essayist. Our object is nearer, namely to discover the part which pure science has played in recent improvements in the art of cultivation and to show that the fertile streams of ideas which refresh the minds of cultivators and bring new sources of power to their use arise in the springs which have origin in the remote regions where pure science broods. It is within the knowledge of all who are interested either in the science or in the practice of Agriculture and Horticulture, that Professor Biffen has succeeded in producing races of wheat which possess the virtues without the defects of the parent races from which they were raised. Thus the new race may possess the power of resisting a disease known as rust together with the capacity to yield a heavy crop. One parent—or ancestor rather—of the new race was a heavy cropper but was so highly susceptible to rust that in seasons when that disease was rampant its fruitfulness was impaired. The other though untroubled by rust could at best yield but poorly. To build up a new race uniting these virtues and free from these defects would seem a simple task; and so it is; but it required half a century of scientific research before the problem proposed itself, and then it required the acumen of one familiar with both the science of Botany and the practice of Agriculture to perceive the possibility and apply the proper method of solving the problem. Let it be remembered by all who are concerned with the interests of the nation that the rôle of pure science is to prophesy and to propound problems. It, no less than poetry, possesses the vision without which the people perish. Not in the individual workers, save in

## DISEASES IN PLANTS

the rare event of the man of science who is a genius; but in pure science itself is the vision. The story of Biffen's discovery will make clear anything that there may seem cryptic in this utterance. About 50 years ago the belief that disease is the maleficent work of evil spirits still lingered in the minds of simple folk. The sophisticated had long abandoned the superstition but were none the wiser in their agnosticism. Simultaneously with the work of Pasteur on the nature of disease in animals, de Bary demonstrated that disease in plants is in the great majority of cases due to the intrusion of a parasite into the body of the plant. He proved moreover that in the case of many diseases the intruder is a fungus and that specific diseases are due to the intrusion of specific fungi. Gradually the co-workers and successors of de Bary arrived at a precise appreciation of the nature of these infectious diseases. As a result of these prolonged labours it is now recognised that it takes *three* to make that quarrel that we call disease: the infecting organism, conditions in the victim which lay it open to or screen it from attack, conditions in the aerial and terrestrial environments which favour either the parasite or the host and so facilitate or discourage attack. The professional mycologist is accustomed to fix his attention too exclusively on the first of these factors, the active agent of disease. The professional cultivator gives habitually great weight to the third and seeks to preserve plants from disease by improving his methods of cultivation. Both are right yet neither is wholly wise, and there is much room in the world for a race of mycologists who not only discover how to cure plants but know how to cultivate them. Biffen seized upon the second of the three factors and envisaged immunity not as an accident but as a grace—a quality inherent in a plant by virtue of which it actively or passively resists a given kind of evil.

Coeval with this stream of knowledge and like it having its sources in the remote fastnesses of pure science another stream commenced to carve out a course for itself through the hard rock of ignorance in which all knowledge has to make and maintain its way. Never was mountain torrent more turbulent than was the science of heredity in its early course. But as the torrent issues in its lower reaches into the navigable river so the science of heredity controlled and canalised by Mendel became a practicable and fertile stream of knowledge. Thanks to the genius of this man we know that if we will discover the laws of inheritance we must fix our attention not on the organism as a whole but upon one and another in turn of the many attributes or characters of that organism. Thus disintegrated the problem of inheritance becomes susceptible of solution by the method of experiment. By applying that method Mendel discovered the simple laws which govern the mode of inheritance of the characters or attributes of living things. Old fashioned men of science may join in chorus with old fashioned men of practice and doubt never so vocally; but it is so; and the best proof of the value of the method lies in the fact that those who know and use it can often show the practical plant breeder the proper way to set to work to secure results which hitherto have baffled his powers. It is essential to our purpose to describe several of the main conclusions reached by Mendel and confirmed by his successors. The first of these is that as the individual derives from two parents and is in that sense a dual thing so is it dual with respect to each of its characters. It may derive the means of developing any one character from both its parents. If so it is pure bred and mating with its like will have issue all of which exhibit the character in question. Or if it descend from parents one of which possessed the character and the other did not, the individual, like a double-barrelled gun, one barrel of which only is loaded, may have only one charge for the expression of the character. Though the one charge may suffice to bring out the character in the individual it will not suffice to establish that character in all his descendants. Mated with his like, that is with another individual in like case with respect to the character, he will produce offspring a fixed proportion of which have the character in question and a fixed proportion of which lack the character.

For the germ cells—the units which join together in pairs to produce the individual, are units in the sense that they lack the dual nature of the individual. They are single-barrelled guns and hence are charged or uncharged. The individual which carries the full double charge gives rise to germ cells all alike with respect to this character. They are all charged. But the individual which carries one charge only gives rise to two kinds of germ cells; half have the charge and half lack it. Hence when the germ cells of two such similar individuals unite in pairs the result can be predicted. On the average in four unions one will be between germ cells charged with the power of developing the character, two between cells one of which is charged and the other not, and one between uncharged germ cells. The first combination will produce an individual pure to the character. Mated with a similar individual he will produce offspring all of which possess the character in question. The second combination will produce an individual which may show the character as markedly as the first; but posterity will betray his hybrid nature: for mated with a similar individual his offspring will be not uniform but divisible into the haves and have-nots as in the case just described. The third combination, of uncharged germ cells, will result in an individual lacking the character, and on the evident principle of *ex nihilo nihil fit* such an individual pure bred

# SUSCEPTIBILITY AND IMMUNITY 123

to the lack of a character mated with a like individual will produce offspring all of which lack the character.

Wherefore it follows that if an individual possessed of an hereditable character (in double dose) mate with another which lacks that character, the offspring will all exhibit that character, but if these offspring mate among themselves their immediate descendants will comprise some which have the character and some which lack it. If the character be an objectionable one, susceptibility to a certain disease, for example, the mating of a susceptible with an immune individual will produce what by every rule of common sense would be called a disastrous result. The offspring will be susceptible and common sense if it had no other guidance would seek elsewhere for the means of eradicating susceptibility to disease from a strain of plants. But seen in the light of Mendelian knowledge the immediate failure of the experiment is a promise of subsequent success. The fact that *all* the plants in the first generation suffer from the disease is evidence that the character —susceptibility to disease—is Mendelian in its behaviour and a sure guarantee that if individuals of the first generation are bred together in pairs their offspring will comprise some which possess and exhibit the immunity of the grandparent. Need it be said that it was by applying this knowledge of the Mendelian laws of inheritance and of the nature of plant disease that

Biffen was able to concentrate in one individual characters belonging to different varieties of wheat—to join together in fruitful union the disease resistance of the one variety and the prolificness of the other!

The combination of characters present in different individuals is fast becoming a routine practice in plant breeding, and the production of such things as early, hardy, marrow fat peas, early-maturing maize, wilt resistant melons, gives certain promise that the science of genetics, founded by Mendel, baptised and proclaimed by Bateson and practised by an ever increasing number of other workers here and abroad, is destined to play a great part in intensive cultivation.

If we turn to consider another important recent discovery, the enhanced fertility of partially sterilized soil, we arrive no less surely at the conclusion that applied science only flourishes in soil rendered fertile by the spade-work of pure science.

The credit of the discovery that soil sterilized or partially sterilized by heat yields larger crops is due to Dr Russell and his co-workers at Rothamstead; for although the advantages of soil-sterilization were known already to sundry growers of plants under glass the benefits accruing to crops as a result of that practice were discovered independently by Russell and first demonstrated and published by him. Moreover Russell pursued his enquiry from results to causes and has been able to propound a simple

## SOIL FERTILITY

hypothesis which fits the known facts so closely as to deserve at least a provisional acceptance. This hypothesis may be described as an inversion of Metchnikoff's doctrine of phagocytosis. Whereas white blood cells—phagocytes—maintain the health of the human body by destroying intruding pathogenic microbes, the protozoa of the soil, according to Russell's hypothesis, by a similar phagocytic action depress the fertility of the soil. A certain number of bacteria is good for a soil and if the numbers fall off the soil becomes sick. As by cauterisation a wound is cleansed, so by partial sterilization the soil is restored to a fertile state. In the former case the bacteria are the sufferers, in the latter the protozoa. In soil and in body alike the struggle is the same but the rôles of the protagonists are reversed. In order to verify the hypothesis and to extend our knowledge of the protozoa of the soil, applied science has most properly applied to zoologists trained in the methods of pure science. On their work must depend much of the success which will attend this novel and promising line of enquiry. Thus in both cases—the dramatic hypothesis of the zoologist Metchnikoff, which emerged from a study of the transparent body of a sick water flea, and the elegant hypothesis of Russell—pure science was present at inception and dénouement. It allured to brighter worlds and led the way.

As a last example of the contribution of pure

science to practical affairs we may trace, albeit only in briefest outline, the recent improvements in the methods of forcing plants. To the layman the subject may appear to be one of only moderate importance; but that view will not be shared by those who know how desirable it is to improve the national dietary, particularly in the seasons when natural growth is dormant. Our knowledge of the methods of awakening plants from their winter rest began with Johannsen's discovery that whereas chloroform or ether vapour anaesthetises the active it quickens the dormant plant. No sooner had market gardeners—the raisers of primeurs—applied this method of etherising to the forcing of flowers and fruit than Molisch discovered the now well known warm bath method of forcing. He proved that in order to quicken a resting plant into growth it suffices to submerge its stem and branches for some hours in tepid water. Yet more recently other investigators have shown that injection of warm water at the base of a bud or even a prick with a needle causes a plant prematurely to resume growth. Finally Stahl and his pupil Lakon have demonstrated that if a plant or cut branch be plentifully supplied with a solution of nutrient (mineral) salts it emerges forthwith from its quiescent winter condition and if placed under suitable conditions of temperature begins to grow in winter as though spring were already come.

Here every step in the advance has been made

by pure science, and it remains for the grower to exploit to the full these means of production not only of luxuries but of food-stuffs which may do much to vary the monotony of our winter diet.

It would seem that the conclusions to be drawn from this brief epitome of progress are that in order to ensure the material prosperity of a nation pure and applied science must advance hand in hand. If with the object of hastening its advance we shower endowment only on applied science and neglect to make provision for the needs of pure science all science will languish. If only from the point of view of a good national investment pure science should receive large encouragement and support from the State. Nor should the encouragement be financial only. A wider source of recruitment must be open to pure science whereby some of the highest ability shall find its way into the ranks of scientific workers and not so exclusively as now to the Temple and India, and parts of Whitehall, Westminster and the City. Leaders in science must for their part be more alive and sympathetic to the applied sciences allied with their own. All the world is their province, and to neglect the pressing problems of the present day is both unwise and unscientific. They should confer in sections in order to review and if necessary to revise the curriculum of science. Thus we should consider the preparation of programmes for the teaching of botany in public schools and should devise means whereby some of our youth training for research obtain a working knowledge of ordinary methods of cultivation. Cultivate the laboratory a little less and our gardens rather more. Discourage the modern sessile habit assumed by students and see to it that the men who are to replace us have wide as well as deep experience. Provision should be made for interchange of students and professors between this country and other parts of the Empire. Train our youth to express themselves both by word of mouth and written word more clearly and convincingly than we have learned to do. Let our Universities provide courses of scientific instruction for the unscientific as well as the purely professional courses. For the sick have need of the physician. The admirable work of the Cambridge University Press in issuing terse and intelligible manuals of scientific discovery should be generally copied; for a wide public exists which desires to know what the researchers are accomplishing, but which requires that the instruction should be given in intelligible English. These are some of the things that we must essay if we are to join with the everlasting duty of seeking truth the pressing need of circulating it—of proselytising the nation.

# SCIENCE IN FORESTRY

By W. Dawson, M.A.

*Reader in Forestry in the University of Cambridge.*

In the primeval forest the ground is irregularly stocked with trees. In one place there is a dense mass of trees intensively engaged in the struggle for existence; in another the ground is stocked with a sparse crop of over-ripe trees, which in time succumbs to age or disease, and then the ground will, under certain conditions, again be covered with young growth. In the over-stocked areas the individual tree is cramped, and as its root has not adequate room for development nor has its crown an adequate supply of light, its increment is hindered. In the course of time, the more vigorous individuals prevail at the expense of the less vigorous, but a period amounting to several decades has passed, in which the individual, which is to form a unit in the final crop, has suffered from the aggression of its neighbours, and only after the loss of much time can it settle down to the business of timber production. What applies to the individual tree, applies to the forest.

The natural forest produces a large crop in a very long time, and when the world had more timber than the nations required this was sufficient. With the industrial development of the present age, however, we find that the consumption of timber is in excess of nature's rate of production, and the consequence is that the available timber supplies are rapidly diminishing. Hitherto we have been able to draw on the accumulated supplies of past ages. In our own country the forests may be said to have long since disappeared. Yet our island climate lends itself peculiarly to tree growth, and in the natural condition perhaps all the land excepting marshes and bare mountain tops was covered with forest. Part of this had to make way for the needs of agriculture, but much more was destroyed for quite uneconomic reasons. The result is, that now less than four per cent. of the land surface bears woodlands and much of that is quite unworthy of the name. We are not a timber producing country. Yet as a great industrial nation we consume vast quantities of timber—over £100,000 worth each day of the year. We import our supplies mainly from Russia, Norway, Sweden and to some extent from Canada and the United States and latterly from Japan. Many causes are contributing to the rapid exhaustion of these supplies. Since 1860 the exports from

## THE SUPPLY OF TIMBER

Russia have increased more than tenfold, from Austria-Hungary sixfold, and from Sweden threefold; and the production in these countries has not increased at all. In the same interval the quantity of timber used in Britain has increased more than threefold; in Germany it is double; and in France the increase amounts to one and a half times. According to calculations of the United States Forestry Department, the annual consumption of timber in that country is three times the annual production. Each of these countries too is demanding more and more timber for her own internal use and, with fresh discoveries as to chemical utilisation of wood, factories are being established where the forests exist and the export of raw timber will be diminished in proportion. All things go to prove that our hitherto reliable sources of supply will cease, and we shall be forced to rear at least a part of our consumption. At present of the coniferous timbers used for railway work, for mining and for building, and general structural purposes, we now produce only about two per cent. of the amount consumed. We have the timber land, many millions of acres of it, quite unfit for agriculture but ideal for forest, now lying more or less waste. We must afforest it, and as mistakes with a crop which takes from half a century to a century to mature are apt to be costly, we cannot afford to adopt slipshod rule-of-thumb methods.

From the nature of things, and in the proper balance of nature, much of our waste land would in the course of time become covered with trees, by natural processes. The trees are prolific in seed-production, and the seeds can germinate and the young trees establish themselves in the most inhospitable of conditions. The balance of nature however has been disturbed. Sheep runs and game preserves occupy much of the land. Deer and even rabbits are preserved, and as soon as nature attempts to reestablish the forest her efforts are defeated. That nature would once more re-afforest the waste lands is demonstrated time and again, and where conditions have been right, self-established forest areas exist. The time is past, however, when we can wait on nature's rate of production. The nations are neither fed nor clothed by the casual production of nature. There is no comparison between the yield of the up-to-date wheat field and the food value given by a like area under natural conditions. So, the forest area must be cultivated and the given space of ground made to render its maximum yield. As time goes on the farmer is becoming more and more dependent on the botanist, the chemist, and the zoologist. The farmer's work provides him with repeated experience of the same problem. He sows and reaps his crop each year, and yet his mere empirical knowledge has long since proved inadequate. Nowadays the cultivation of timber crops is as much a necessity as the cultivation of food-stuffs. The forester, however, deals with a crop which takes the best part of a century to mature, and in the nature of things he cannot experience more than the fringes of the matter. The mere empiricist must stop much less than half way. The forester, in the modern conditions, is in many ways taking liberties with nature, and if he is not versed in the scientific principles which underlie his work, he will surely be defeated. The forester must apply the principles of many sciences. He must have the aid of the botanist. He must know the life-histories of the trees, and he must know the principles on which they grow. He must know the conditions needed by the "light demanders," and he must know the conditions under which the "shade-bearers" will give their maximum yield, in the minimum time. He must know which trees will associate with others, and which trees are intolerant of any but their own kind. Empirical knowledge of these facts cannot be acquired in the time at the forester's disposal. Then even in the natural conditions the trees are subject to the attacks of parasitic fungi which cause the destruction of the timber and lead to the death of the trees. In the artificial commercial forest the conditions favour the development of those diseases, and if events are allowed to take their course the forest may be destroyed. Under present conditions in this country it is not possible to estimate what the financial loss from such causes may be, owing to the lack of system and the lack of records of all things relating to our woods; but in the case of a single disease, *Trametes pini*, it is calculated that the loss on the annual cut, in Prussia alone, exceeds £50,000. The fungus, *Hysterium pinastri*, often devastates the seed-beds and causes the death of millions of seedlings. Other diseases are so aggressive that it is hardly possible to rear to maturity any specimens of the host tree, as for example *Peridermium strobi* on Weymouth Pine. There are also hosts of diseases which do damage in a lesser degree. The prevention and cure of such diseases cannot be discovered by practice alone. Careful investigation in the laboratory is necessary in order that we may discover the intimate life-history of the fungus. The plant pathologist may work to discover the bare facts of the life-history, but the discovery of these facts will point the way to the practical eradication of the disease. A single laboratory discovery could save the country many thousands of pounds each year.

There is perhaps no question of greater importance in tree growth than that of heredity. It has for long been the custom, in the practice, to get the seed for future timber crops in the cheapest market and with the least trouble, and in the case of the bulk of the planted woodlands of the present day the planter has no knowledge of the characteristics of the parent trees, or the least idea where the

# HEREDITY

original seed came from. There has always been a vague idea in the forester's mind that the seed might transmit the characteristics of the parent tree, but in the absence of exact information the question was left at that. In recent times, the investigations of Engler, of Cieslar and of Mayr have thrown some light on the question, and though results have not always been consistent, sufficient has been demonstrated to show the futility of promiscuity. Engler's experiments at Zürich show that seeds collected from different types of the same species carry the characteristics of the parents to the new generation when the lots of seeds are grown under similar conditions, in circumstances ideal to the species. His experiments which have been conducted over a considerable number of years show most striking results. Mayr contended that the young trees, after a few years of growth in the new environment, assumed the typical growth of the species in that environment, but his experiments were cut short by his death. Experience in this country goes to support Engler's contentions. The question opens up enormous possibilities which can only be dealt with by the trained botanical investigator. That the present species *Pinus silvestris*, L. (the Scots Pine) embraces a number of forms or strains or types, whatever one may call them, is certain. The native Scots Pine of North Scotland is different from the Scots Pine of South England, and different from the

Scots Pine of South Germany and of France. It closely resembles the pine of Scandinavia and of Finland. They differ in colour of needle and in habit of growth, and what is of most importance in character and quality of timber. The native *P. silvestris* L. of North Scotland tends to grow with a quite straight stem, while the other varieties even when grown under close canopy, in ideal silvicultural conditions, have a marked tendency to corkscrew form of growth. The bark (which is an indicator of quality of timber) differs. The timber itself is markedly different. In the one case the heart-wood is golden yellow in colour and of large proportion, while in the other it is dull red and small. It may be asserted that these differences are explained by climatic influences, but distinct climatic varieties do not arise in a single generation, and a generation of tree life is a century or two. Mayr held that the differences were so marked and of such importance as to justify the separation of the pine native to North Scotland, Scandinavia and Finland, which he named *Pinus laponica*. Yet the forester purchases the seed from anywhere, and as seed collecting is not an organised business in this country more likely than not his supplies will come from South Germany or from France where seed collecting is attended to. In the last fifty years, much evil has resulted to this country from the importation of seed from any cheap source, and in the native pine districts

## HYBRID TREES

in Scotland, woodlands showing all the inferior characteristics of the southern "variety" are now to be found alongside of the superior variety native to the soil. Thus, in the absence of distinct data as to the origin of the various planted woods, the question is complicated, but there is all the greater demand for thorough scientific investigation. What is true of Scots Pine is undoubtedly true of other species. While the selection of seed in agriculture has been proved to be of the greatest importance, it is clear that it is more so in forestry; for the agriculturist has the opportunity of putting things right in a single year, but the silviculturist is committed to a century. The forester is helpless in the matter, and the skilled botanical investigator must solve the problem.

The work which has been done in producing new varieties of agricultural plants suggests the possibility of producing new varieties of trees. Hybrids carry with them certain advantages; they are generally more rapid and vigorous in growth. Some steps have already been taken in the direction of producing hybrid trees, and the results have been startling. It is possible to produce much greater bulk of timber in a given time, or to produce the desired bulk of timber in a very much shorter time. Anything which can shorten the rotation is of the utmost value in commercial forestry, for it must be borne in mind that the capital expense of planting is lying out at compound interest throughout the rotation, and if that extends beyond a certain period the result will be loss instead of gain. There is a common belief that all quickly grown timbers are of inferior quality. This is not the case; it holds good only as regards durability in the case of coniferous timber, but does not hold good in respect of any quality in ash, oak, and walnut. Further, as regards the conifers it is now possible artificially to increase the durability of the most inferior to a point which makes them far superior to the naturally durable timbers untreated. With oak, ash, walnut, etc., the quicker their growth, the better is their quality in every way. They are more durable, more elastic and less difficult to work. Further by hybridizing it may be possible to produce disease-resisting varieties, and varieties carrying with them other desirable characteristics. The small amount of work already done in the way of hybridizing serves to prove the possibilities, and distinctly points the way to scientific discoveries of great value.

What is true of plant diseases, is equally definitely demonstrated in the case of insect enemies. The artificial forest favours the rapid multiplication of the insects which prey on trees. Ideal breeding and feeding grounds are provided, and the natural enemies of the insects are often destroyed. It is on record that in the period 1892-96, more

## INSECT PESTS

than 25,000 acres of pine woods in the neighbourhood of Nuremberg were utterly destroyed by the caterpillar of *Fidonia piniaria*. In Bohemia between 1872–76, 175,000,000 cubic feet of spruce was killed by the bark beetle, *Tomicus typographus*. In 1890–92 no less than 15,000 acres of spruce immediately north of Munich was stripped bare of needles and killed by the nun moth *Liparis monacha*. A few years later the very existence of the Saxon woods was threatened. Twenty years earlier at least a thousand acres in Poland and in Russia were devastated. The history of continental forestry is full of records of such incidents. To convince the forester of this country of the dangers of insect attacks one has only to mention the pine weevil *Hylobius abietis*. This insect if left to itself can undo the most careful work of the forester. In the ideal conditions presented by a new plantation on land which still bears the undecayed stumps of felled trees, the insects appear from somewhere and multiply with amazing rapidity. Their food is the tender bark of the young trees. They eat it down to the cambium layer and the trees may be killed. Land which has been attacked and on which no preventive measures have been taken has invariably to be replanted, and in many cases, where the persistence is commendable but the lack of knowledge lamentable, replanting has had to be done not only twice but even three and four times. The cost of each replanting is lost money. In fact the loss caused by this insect in our woodlands amounts to many thousand pounds each year. Formerly it was the custom to wait for a period of seven years before replanting ground from which coniferous timber had been removed. The accepted belief was that the ground needed this period of rest; but untrained observation is faulty. The real explanation is that this insect was infesting the ground unobserved, and was making growth impossible. The result of the "rest" was that seven years' increment and rent were lost, moreover bare forest land rapidly degenerates by exposure, and by the growth of weeds, etc., it becomes yearly more difficult and expensive to plant. The total loss was thus large. Now that scientific investigation has shown us the life-history of the insect, it has been possible to devise means, still somewhat clumsy however, by which the multiplication of the insect can be kept in check, and newly cleared ground can be replanted with comparative safety. At present investigation is proceeding and doubtless fresh means will be devised. It is not unreasonable to expect that the entomologist will enable us completely to master these insect pests. A possible solution of the problem may be the discovery of parasites which would prey on the dangerous insects, and even cause epidemics leading to their partial destruction. The forester unaided

## SOIL CONDITIONS

is helpless. He must have the assistance of the entomologist.

In questions of pure silviculture too, where there is reasonable ground for assuming that practice would be sufficient, the forester is dependent on the laboratory investigator. Questions as to the capacity of certain soils to grow certain trees are settled on broad lines by experience. Nevertheless it is frequently found that trees planted on soils which generally speaking should suit them, may fail. The soil may have all the ingredients in sufficient quantity necessary for the growth of the trees, and yet the trees either will not establish themselves, or after a brief period their normal growth ceases. This experience is most commonly met with in the case of plantations on moorlands, and has nothing to do, either with the fertility of the soil or climatic conditions. The presence of the various kinds of "pan" goes far to explain things, but further knowledge is wanted. Extensive investigations have taken place on the continent, notably by Dr Müller in Denmark, and some light has been thrown on the question. Its solution will be of particular interest to us, as it has become imperative that we increase our forest area, and it is mainly on the moorlands that this must take place.

As a result of faulty observation, forestry is not infrequently worked on lines which defeat the desired end. It has for long been the custom to start new plantations by planting the young trees very close together, often at intervals of three feet or less. In continuation of the same principle, the plantations have often been insufficiently thinned. It is already proved that close planting gives a smaller yield of timber than moderately wide planting, while it costs a great deal more. Further, without investigation we do not know to what degree and at what periods thinnings should be carried out. Ocular impressions of the condition of things are wholly misleading, as the present condition of any immature wood is only of importance in so far as it affects the final yield. Hence more exact methods have to be employed, and it is surprising to what extent forestry has already become mathematical. The tree and the forest have been analysed, and the relationship of the contents at any period to the contents at subsequent periods can be seen, and thus the result of any operation on the subsequent life of the forest can be predicted.

Forestry does not aim at merely producing wood but must produce wood of the desired quality. Hence the branch of science, which is known as "Timber Physics," has a distinct bearing on the forester's work. Knowledge of the relationship of the growing conditions to the quality and technical characteristics of the wood produced, would enable the forester to proceed intelligently in his work, and to some extent to control the quality of the

## TIMBER PHYSICS 143

timber. Laboratory investigation into the variations of structure and mechanical properties in timbers from the same kind of tree can show us how far these variations are due to the different silvicultural conditions under which the timbers were produced. A considerable amount of work has already been done, but in such investigations complete results are exceedingly difficult to get.

Much of the timber used (over £40,000,000 in value a year) is used for outdoor work such as fencing posts, railway sleepers, telegraph poles, mining timber, etc., where it is liable to decay. The high price of the timber and the steadily rising demand make the question of increasing the durability of the timber one of vital importance. It is clear that if the life of the timber could be doubled, only half as much timber would be needed. Green timber decays most rapidly and hence the first preservative measure was to season it before use, but no matter how well seasoned the wood may be, if it be exposed to outside conditions it can again absorb moisture and so be exposed to disease as before. For some time now it has been customary to impregnate the timber with substances which render the cell contents unsuitable for fungus growth, and which coat the cell walls and prevent their absorbing water. The processes employed are various and the substances which have been most extensively employed are creosote, zinc chloride, bichloride of mercury, and copper sulphate. Creosote is by far the most effective, and by its use the life of the timber can be multiplied many times. Processes can be greatly improved and probably cheaper preservatives discovered. This means that woods which are naturally non-durable and have been considered worthless can be rendered equal in value to superior kinds. There will thus be less waste in the woods, and the forester will be able to grow the species of tree best suited to his soil and climate, even though that tree has hitherto been considered of inferior value.

The work of the chemist has a further direct bearing on the production of the forest, for the industrial chemistry of wood has developed enormously in recent times. Already the capital invested in plant for this work amounts to many million pounds, and the annual consumption of timber represents the growth of many thousands of acres. Germany alone uses 15,000,000–20,000,000 cubic feet a year. Among the substances produced by the destructive distillation of wood are methyl alcohol, amyl alcohol, ether, acetone, formaldehyde, acetic, propionic and other acids, as well as various tars. Further discoveries are being made and these industries will assume still larger proportions. There is thus a sure and ever-increasing market for the forest produce and, what is of more importance in some cases, material which is unfit for building timber can be utilized, and material

## FORESTRY A COMPOSITE SUBJECT 145

which would otherwise be waste turned to proper account.

Forestry is a composite subject applying the principles of many sciences, and the only hope for its advancement lies in the close partnership of the laboratory investigator and the practical forester.

# SYSTEMATIZED PLANT BREEDING

By R. H. Biffen, F.R.S.

*Professor of Agricultural Botany in the
University of Cambridge*

It is impracticable within the limits of a short essay to give in adequate detail an account of the investigations now carried on in the Plant Breeding Institute attached to the School of Agriculture. All that need be said of them is that they have as their object the improvement of the various crops grown by the farmers of this country. I propose to confine myself to the work carried out with the wheat crop and further to describe only those portions having a direct bearing on the supply of home-grown grain, omitting those of more or less theoretic interest which would only appeal to students of the modern subject of genetics. The work owes its origin primarily to a desire to know whether Mendel's now well-known laws of inheritance applied to other plants than the various kinds of peas he used in his experiments. It developed rapidly in directions unforeseen at the time and led, as the sequel will show, into many curious bypaths. Now it has become almost a

## WHEAT BREEDING

matter of routine. Meanwhile the small experimental plots, originally sufficient for a purely genetical investigation, have grown and grown until a special farm is required to accommodate them, whilst plant for cleaning and milling the grain and finally converting it into bread has had to be installed. Growth too has taken place in other directions, for former students are applying the knowledge they have gained in the Institute to the solution of problems, somewhat similar to our own, in the colonies and in other wheat-producing countries of the world, using for this purpose wheats which have been raised here in the course of our experiments.

Wheat breeding it is true is no new subject, for even at the commencement of these investigations work was in progress in Canada and especially in Australia. In the latter country it was in the hands of a former student of this University, the late Mr William Farrer of New South Wales. His work has left an indelible impress on that country, for not only has it provided it with wheats of superb quality but also with varieties which can be grown commercially in districts where wheat growing, for various reasons, was previously impossible. Farrer's success, however, and this is written in no spirit of depreciation, was due to his endless patience and that happy gift some breeders have acquired of recognising the merits of one individual plant amongst thousands and selecting it as the basis of a new variety. In such work chance plays an important part, whilst the aim of the breeder of to-day is to eliminate chance and work definitely for the end in view. A brief consideration of one of Mendel's experiments will show how this can be effected. He crossed together two varieties of garden peas, one having round, yellow seeds, the other green and wrinkled seeds. From the hybrids he ultimately obtained four strains of peas; one with round yellow seeds, one with round green seeds, one with wrinkled green and one with wrinkled yellow seeds. Two of these resemble the original parents in their seed characters, whilst two, namely those with round green and those with wrinkled yellow seeds, are, as far as this experiment is concerned, new forms. These novelties arise from a reshuffling of the parental characteristics, and further each character, whether roundness or wrinkledness, yellowness or greenness, appears in the new forms in the same intensity as in the original parents. With these facts before one it needed little imagination to realise that if the results obtained by Mendel in his cloister gardens with peas could be obtained with wheat then definite plans could be made for building up into one variety the useful characteristics to be found amongst the almost innumerable varieties in cultivation in various parts of the world.

Experiments were started therefore with the idea of testing this possibility, and in the course of a few years the manner of inheritance of most of the characteristics distinguishing the numerous wheat varieties was traced in some detail. In the course of the investigations it became clear that the building up of fresh combinations of these characters so as to form new varieties was a simple matter. Given for instance such a problem as raising a variety characterised by the possession of a rough and red chaff, a combination of features not occurring amongst English wheats, this could be effected by crossing such a rough chaffed wheat as Old Hoary with any smooth, red chaffed form such as Square Head's Master, and further the new variety could be obtained in a form breeding true to type in as short a period as four years. From a technical point of view, however, the information obtained had singularly little value, for the morphological characteristics of the wheats with which the systematists are concerned have little interest for the farmer. It is true that he prefers a beardless to a bearded wheat, for the awns are a nuisance if the chaff has to be fed to cattle, he may also prefer a smooth-chaffed variety to a rough-chaffed one, thinking that the hairs on the glumes may retain the moisture during showery weather and so cause the grain to sprout, or again he often has more or less aesthetic preferences for certain shapes of the ear or colour, yet broadly speaking morphological features have as a whole no really important significance to him. His one real concern is to obtain the greatest possible value for his crop, and as our food supply is partially dependent on this we may agree that his object is a meritorious one.

Plans were accordingly made to test the possibility of using Mendel's principles to build up fresh combinations of the somewhat elusive features which go to the making of a wheat which the farmer would consider good enough to displace the kinds he already grows. These wheats have some excellent features, the most prominent of which is that if well cultivated they are capable of producing very high yields of grain and straw per acre. On discussing the possibility of improving wheats with farmers it was found that they attached more importance to this feature than to any other, and without exception took the line that still heavier yields per acre should be tried for. On the face of it the solution of the problem seems impossible. If one may assume that high and low cropping capacity form a pair of Mendelian characteristics then the expectation would be that a cross between two varieties showing these characteristics would ultimately produce new types with the yielding capacity of one or other of the parents. But more than one indirect line of attack was open. The yield per acre is dependent on several distinct factors, the most important of which, since they are more or less controllable, are the supply of food materials available for the growing plant and

## THE STIFFNESS OF STRAW

secondly the losses caused by parasites, mainly of a fungoid nature. The former factor hardly appears to concern the plant breeder but in practice it does, for supplementing the supplies of food material present in the soil by the addition of natural or artificial manures frequently leads to over-vigorous growth of the foliage and of stems which cannot withstand rough weather conditions. The crop is then "laid" and not only is it expensive to harvest but the yield is often seriously depreciated. This is particularly the case in the Fens where a season hardly ever passes without a great proportion of the crop being so badly laid that it is impossible to cut it with self-binders. Consequently the production of a variety capable of standing well under conditions of intensive cultivation is a matter of great importance. A comparison of existing varieties whilst growing under the same conditions of cultivation shows that considerable differences exist in the stiffness of the straw. Yet none are as rigid as one could wish. But amongst the hybrids from some of the lesser known varieties straws have been found which are stiffer than any at present in cultivation. These forms have been used successfully for building up new types and in the immediate future several varieties particularly suitable for intensive cultivation should be available. One indeed has already been placed on the market.

The losses caused by disease are far more serious

than is generally realised even amongst the growers themselves. To a certain extent these losses can be avoided, as for instance those caused by the attacks of the smut fungus which can be reduced to a negligible quantity by a preliminary treatment of the grain before sowing. Other fungoid diseases of which the common yellow rust is a conspicuous example are uncontrollable and year by year they take a very appreciable toll of the crop. What this amounts to on the average it is impossible to say at all definitely, but an estimate of from five to ten per cent. is probably not very wide of the real figures. The farmer as a rule pays little attention to its presence, partly because he knows that nothing can be done to prevent it and partly because the attacks never completely cripple the crop in this country. I have even come across cases where the farmer has rather welcomed an attack on the grounds that the leaves died off early and readily separated from the straw during the threshing of the crop. Such ideas would soon disappear if one could but gauge more accurately the part played by each of the various factors determining the yield of the crop. Where for instance a promising plant fails to produce the yield anticipated in the earlier stages of its growth the loss caused by rust is all too often put down vaguely to the weather or to that mysterious blight responsible for most of the crop failures in this and other countries. To any one at all familiar with the losses caused even

# FARRER'S EXPERIMENTS 153

by mild epidemics of fungoid disease it was very evident that if anything could be done to prevent, or even to mitigate them, then in the aggregate the results would prove of great value. Experiments were therefore started with the object of testing the possibility of breeding rust-resisting varieties of wheat. The idea was not a new one, for Farrer had already made the attempt. His work however was pre-Mendelian and based on the fact that an $F_2$[1] generation contained, as a rule, a large number of distinct types. Amongst these Farrer hoped to find some showing a greater degree of rust-resistance than any of the varieties he then had under cultivation. His optimism was rewarded, for he found amongst them the variety "Bobs" which possesses a very fair degree of resistance to the attacks of the black rust, the common species in Australia and several other important wheat-growing countries, but a species of little importance here at present. Farrer's experiments were not planned with any object of testing the possibility of definitely breeding for rust-resistance, neither had he apparently satisfactory material at hand for the purpose.

The first steps in the investigation were taken by comparing the rust-resistance of several hundred distinct varieties of wheat grown under uniform

---

[1] The letter F followed by the figure 1 is used to denote the actual hybrid plant, and successive generations raised from it are denoted by $F_2$, $F_3$, $F_4$, etc.

conditions. These determinations were repeated for several years and it was found that the varieties could be grouped into a number of arbitrary classes showing either no disease at all, traces, or slight, moderate, or bad attacks. This classification was found to hold from year to year, the varieties always falling into the same groups as those in which they had been included in former seasons, and this in spite of the varying intensity of the attack in the different years. Amongst the set was one variety, found originally as a single plant in a plot of Northern Duluth wheat, which year by year was absolutely free from pustules of yellow rust and which still after twelve years' cultivation here retains its striking immunity. This variety known under its notebook name of "American Club" was crossed with Michigan Bronze, the most susceptible variety which could be found amongst those under trial. The resulting $F_1$ plants proved to be exceedingly susceptible to the attacks of yellow rust. In this respect they were indistinguishable from Michigan Bronze, but either the attack was not in reality as severe or possibly because of the extra vigour of the hybrids a fairly good crop of grain was secured. From this an $F_2$ generation of over 2000 plants was raised in the following year. An inspection of the plots in the early summer soon made it clear that the power of resisting the attacks of yellow rust was an inheritable character, for standing out clearly amongst the mass of the

## RUST-RESISTANCE 155

most afflicted plants one could well imagine were numbers of individuals with healthy green foliage. Their leaves and stems were dusted over with the loose spores shed from neighbouring plants, but in spite of every chance of becoming infected they remained without a single rust pustule until the crop was ready for harvest. Although one sees similar cases yearly the novelty of it still remains, and I often wonder at the almost Eastern composure with which a number of our distinguished visitors from the London Conference of Genetics examined these plots plant by plant.

On determining the numbers of rusty and healthy plants they were found to be present in the proportion of approximately three of the former to one of the latter class (1609 to 523). The approximation was sufficiently close to indicate that rust resistance was, in Mendelian language, a recessive character and that consequently these resistant plants would breed true to this feature in the next and in succeeding generations. An extensive series of trials proved that this was the case. Several hundred cultures were raised from resistant and susceptible individuals with the result that the former class yielded resistant plants only, whilst the latter either bred true to extreme susceptibility or produced a susceptible and resistant offspring, again in the proportion of three to one. At this stage then we had the first proof that the plant breeder if given a suitable starting point in the form of varieties resistant to any special disease could at will transfer this immunity to other varieties and so play a part in its control. It is too early to say how far these results will hold with regard to other diseases but in two other cases which have been tested fairly thoroughly, namely a mildew on barley and a second rust on wheat, similar results have been obtained.

The next step was to arrange a demonstration of the facts for our critical friends the farmers. This took the form of small plots one yard square sown with four types isolated from the cultures of the previous year. Two of the types resembled the parents, one having the dense ears of American Club and its rust resistance, the other the lax ears of Michigan Bronze and its extreme susceptibility to disease. The other two showed resistance in association with lax ears and susceptibility with dense ears, or to put the matter more simply they were immune forms of Michigan Bronze and susceptible forms of American Club. The plots were arranged draught-board fashion with the resistant and susceptible forms alternating in each row of squares. During the summer months the regular patchwork of orange and green formed a striking demonstration of the possibility of definitely breeding for rust resistance. At harvest too they gave some idea of the losses which a severe epidemic can cause, for whilst the resistant plots produced

# LITTLE JOSS WHEAT

an average crop, say of about 32 bushels per acre, the susceptible plots only gave a yield of the order of a single bushel per acre. Unfortunately the death of the susceptible forms after a couple of years' cultivation put a stop to the further continuation of this demonstration.

Concurrently with these experiments an attempt was made to put the results to some practical use, and a series of wheats were bred from a resistant Russian variety found amongst some Ghurka wheats. Amongst these was one now known under the name of Little Joss which has proved of some importance. Its other parent was Square Head's Master, perhaps the most widely cultivated wheat in the country. Even in the $F_4$ stage the hybrid appeared to be cropping more heavily than its English parent and it was evidently far better in this respect than the Russian variety, which indeed was not suitable for cultivation under our conditions. Comparative trials of the hybrid and Square Head's Master were therefore made on a large scale at the first opportunity with results that left no doubt that the hybrid was distinctly the better variety. Corroboration of these results is to be found in an independent set of trials carried out at the Experimental Station at Snoring in Norfolk. The trials over a period of seven years show that its yield is some four bushels per acre better than that of the other varieties tested, these being the pick of the English and French wheats. The actual figures, neglecting fractions, are 40 and 36 bushels of 63 lbs. each per acre. The results can be explained on the assumption that the hybrid has inherited the yielding capacity of Square Head's Master together with the disease-resisting property of the Ghurka wheat, and consequently rust takes no toll of the crop as it always does in varying amounts of a crop of Square Head's Master. The preliminary trials made it clear that the wheat was one which was suitable in other respects, such as in the yield of straw, its standing-capacity under bad conditions, its time of ripening, and so on, and it was therefore distributed on a small scale amongst farmers in the Eastern counties. At the same time arrangements were made to secure reports as to its yield per acre under the diverse conditions it met with away from the experimental farm. An analysis of these results shows conclusively that the original estimates made of its cropping capacity were fairly correct, for the yields average from five to ten per cent. per season more than Square Head's Master. Fortunately, for this is a matter outside the breeder's control at present, the variety has proved adaptable for all types of soils on which wheat can be grown, though perhaps it succeeds best on the lighter and poorer soils. As a result it has become thoroughly established, especially in the Eastern counties where it forms the bulk of the wheat now grown. Its cultivation has extended steadily to other parts of the country, and now one can hardly travel a few miles in arable districts when the corn is ripening without recognising its distinctive rich red chaff and highly polished straw.

Though the resistance of Little Joss to yellow rust is very marked it is not as complete as that of American Club. But the hybrids of this latter variety have not yet reached the stage at which they can be distributed generally and consequently independent trials of their value cannot be quoted. All that can be said at present is that they fulfil expectations and that there is every possibility of their displacing the one rust-resisting type now in cultivation here.

The experimental work with these rust-resistant wheats is gradually bringing to light other points of interest associated with this feature. It is now becoming clear that rust attacks are partly, though by no means entirely, responsible for weakness of the straw. In varieties which are particularly badly attacked the straw always becomes light and spongy in texture, these faults increasing with the severity of the attack. Such enfeebled straws cannot possibly carry a heavy crop of grain even if the plants could produce one. The fact is of some immediate importance, for intensive cultivation, one of the crying needs of the future, will inevitably make for increasingly severe attacks of rust and other fungoid diseases. At present our crops are grown with little more than the food materials naturally present in well worked soils. Increasing these supplies by the application of so-called artificial manures has marked effects on the intensity of a rust attack. Phosphates and to a less extent potash salts tend to restrict its severity, but the application of the essential nitrogenous manures, whether in the form of nitrate of soda, sulphate of ammonia, guano or any other form, tends to increase its severity to such an extent that disease becomes an exceedingly important limiting factor. None of the methods tried up to the present offer the slightest promise of checking this tendency. But direct experiments on this point show that the high degree of resistance, amounting practically to immunity, possessed by American Club and some of its hybrids is retained to the full even when far larger applications of nitrogenous manures are made to the soil in which they are growing than any one farming for profit would think of using.

Unfortunately resistance to the attacks of one rust does not necessarily imply resistance to the attacks of other species, so that our resistant wheats are of no value in countries where the prevalent species is other than the common yellow rust. Even in countries such as India where this species is excessively abundant our wheats are useless, for they fail to mature with sufficient rapidity. If sown at the same time as the Indian wheats they come into flower a month later so that they cannot even be used for hybridising purposes. But the difficulty of using these varieties as a basis for building up rust-resisting Indian wheats has been circumvented by sowing the Indian wheats here in the spring, when they flower at the same time as our autumn sown crops. Hybrids are then raised between them and the $F_2$ generations sown in India provide the material from which selections suitable for that country can be made.

Another of the great failings of English wheat is found in its lack of quality. All of the varieties grown here are characterised by producing indifferent loaves for which it would be difficult to find any market now-a-days. When the flour is made up into dough the gas formed during the fermentation processes brought about by the yeast leaks freely, with the result that the volume of the loaf is small and the bread is lacking in lightness. Moreover the loaf tends to flatten out rather than to rise when placed in the oven. A considerable proportion of the wheat which we have to import is on the other hand particularly well suited for the manufacture of the type of loaf now universally demanded. The characteristic tough dough from the flour of these wheats retains the gas well, with the result that it swells strongly during fermentation, and further the loaves do not collapse in the oven. Such wheats are known technically as "strong" wheats. In consequence of the relative shortness of their supply they command considerably higher prices than wheats of the kinds grown here, which for the sake of convenience we may describe as "weak" wheats. In normal times when English wheat is selling at say 35$s.$ several of the imported strong wheats will usually command 39$s.$ or 40$s.$ per quarter. The miller is forced to purchase these more costly wheats in order to utilise the English crop. This is done by blending the strong imported and weak native types in suitable proportions and then grinding them together. The question at once arose, whether it was practicable to grow strong wheats in this country for given an equality in the crop they would be worth somewhere about a sovereign per acre more to the farmer. No evidence could be obtained as to the possibility of this. The farmers had no real experience of the cultivation of wheats as strong as those imported from Canada, for instance, and they were frankly sceptical as to the value of even attempting the experiment. They contended that the miller now gave very little more, if anything, for the wheats which they considered to be of good quality, and at the best the difference was so slight that it paid them far better to grow the greatest possible crop regardless of quality. The millers on the other hand had a very strong case, for they could show conclusively that the change of public taste brought about by the importation of strong wheat during the last generation

# ENGLISH AND CANADIAN WHEATS 163

had made the differences of quality to which they formerly attached some significance practically negligible. These differences were of the order of two or three per cent., whilst the difference between weak English and strong foreign wheats was far and away greater. It is almost impossible to give anyone unfamiliar with the niceties of judging bread a clear idea of them, though perhaps the following figures will help in the matter. In the baking experiments necessary in the course of this investigation the loaves are marked on a more or less arbitrary scale, points being assigned for volume, height, the character of the crust and the texture of the crumb. An average sample of flour from English wheat generally earns some 50 or 60 points, whilst flour suitable for the preparation of ordinary bread, or flour of the "London Households" standard, gets about 80. Still better grades used only for special purposes may be marked as high as 100 or even, but very exceptionally, more. The best grades of Canadian wheat, that is typical strong wheats, generally earn from 85 to 95 on this scale, the differences depending largely on the harvest conditions obtaining in Canada from season to season. But if one could obtain no evidence as to the possibility of growing this kind of wheat in the country one met with plenty of criticisms regarding the uselessness of attempting to do so, based on the belief then prevalent that strength was determined by the conditions under which the crop was grown, and the assumption was always made that our climate positively forbade the production of strong wheats. It seemed impossible to put much trust in this view, for different critics assumed that the notorious lack of strength in English wheats was determined by such different factors as lack of sunshine or an excessive rainfall, or again by the fact that our soil conditions are very different to those of the virgin lands of Canada which produce so much of the best wheat we import. The matter was evidently one for investigation.

The experiments were carried out mainly by the Home-grown Wheat Committee of the National Association of British and Irish Millers, with whom I had the good fortune to come in touch at an early stage of my work, and to whom I am indebted for much technical information which cannot readily be acquired by the ordinary student. The method employed after collecting a considerable number of varieties of imported wheat was to mill and bake a part of each parcel in order to determine its strength as grown abroad and to sow the remainder. The resulting crop was then tested as before and in most cases sowings for further testing were made again. The upshot of a long series of trials has shown that most varieties deteriorate markedly in strength when grown under our conditions, and in a year or so they are little if any better than ordinary English

## STRENGTH AND CLIMATE

wheats. But there are exceptions, and some few wheats have been found which retain their strength perfectly even when grown year after year in this country. In fact in one case we now know of a variety which has endured our climatic conditions for some five and twenty years without being any the worse for it. It has to be recognised then that there are two kinds of strength, though it is impossible to distinguish between them at present, one which is determined by external conditions, the other which is as characteristic of the variety as such features as chaff, colour or awns. An example of the first class of strong wheats is provided by Tisra Videki, an exceptionally strong wheat from Hungary. Some of the parcels of this variety are possibly the finest wheat from the standpoint of quality ever grown. In two years, however, its strength sinks to practically that of ordinary English wheat. It is impossible to say why, and the only result an enquiry into the subject has produced is the interesting one that English wheat sent to Hungary and grown on the fields which have produced some of the best samples of Tisra Videki have not improved appreciably in quality after growing for three years under the same conditions. The Canadian Red Fife is an example of the second class. Well grown and well harvested samples are so similar in strength to the best of those imported from Canada that one cannot distinguish between them in the baking trials. Moreover we appear to be justified in looking upon the quality of this wheat as being one of its distinguishing characteristics, for it has proved to be strong when grown in Australia, India and in S. Africa. The one objection that has been raised to this view is that Fifes as grown in the Pacific States of America are distinctly lacking in strength. A recent test of these varieties has, however, shown that whatever else these wheats may be they are not Fife wheats, for not only do they differ in strength but also in several very obvious morphological features. The discovery that Red Fife retained its strength when grown in this country led to many trials to determine whether it was suitable for general cultivation here. These have shown that there is no likelihood of its ever being grown widely, for it rarely crops satisfactorily. In some districts however its yield is as good as that of our own varieties and occasionally it gives really excellent crops, in one case as much as 59 bushels per acre. Where this is the case the wheat is now well established and its produce meets with a good demand at fair prices from local millers. These local successes effectively dispose of the statement, so frequently made, that strong wheat cannot be grown at a profit in this country.

Whilst the question of the possibility of growing strong wheats here was under investigation experiments were started to determine whether strength

## ESTIMATION OF STRENGTH

was an inheritable characteristic. By some lucky accident Red Fife was chosen as one of the wheats from which hybrids were to be raised, for we did not know at the time that it would retain its quality under our conditions. The problem on which so much turns is one which presents many difficulties to the plant-breeder. In the first place we have no methods of determining with absolute certainty whether a wheat is strong or not except by milling and baking it. Such tests involve the use of large quantities of grain. Baking trials are not at the best extremely accurate, and with unknown flours several trials have often to be made in order to hit off the best methods of handling the doughs. As a result one has to be prepared to sacrifice about half a hundredweight of grain in order to secure a result which is accurate within one or two per cent. This degree of precision is, as we have frequently found by the addition of duplicates in a series of trials, attained by a skilled baker familiar with the intricacies of testing work. Such an amount of grain is, however, beyond the resources of a plant-breeder in the earlier stages of his work, as for instance in the $F_2$ generations where he requires to know the strength of the grain of individual plants, though with good management it can be obtained in the $F_4$ generations. In practice, as for instance when purchasing imported wheats, strength is largely judged by the appearance of the sample. The points to which attention is paid are the translucency and the hardness of the grain, since these features are commonly associated with strength whilst weak wheats are most frequently opaque and readily crushed. An experienced buyer can grade wheats with fair accuracy by inspection only, but the grading appears to be dependent on an unconscious recognition of the varieties in question and a previous knowledge of their milling and baking properties. Failing a baking test, wheats may be roughly graded for quality, and the extremes of strong and weak wheats may be separated with certainty by determining the toughness and hence the gas-retaining properties of the gluten. This is effected by chewing some twenty or thirty grains until the starch disappears under the action of the saliva and the grain coats have been swallowed unconsciously If the resulting pellet of gluten is tough and elastic it may be assumed that the variety is strong, if on the other hand it is soft and snaps when stretched slightly weakness is indicated. The method is a good one, but only those who have sorted out an $F_2$ generation of a couple of hundred plants can realise how tedious it is in actual use.

The first crosses made with a view of investigating the inheritance of strength were between Red Fife and Rough Chaff. The parents under our conditions produce grain which can be classified with considerable certainty, for the Red Fife is

## INHERITANCE OF STRENGTH

always hard and translucent whilst the Rough Chaff is always opaque, soft and floury. Moreover in the mill and bakehouse these varieties are also very distinct from one another. The differences are difficult to describe in non-technical terms, but they are so marked that the veriest amateur can distinguish between the flours, the doughs and the bread from the two varieties. They provided therefore more or less ideal material for the investigation of the inheritance of strength. The $F_2$ generation of the cross showed segregation into strong and weak forms roughly in the proportion of three of the former to one of the latter. A series of individual plants from this generation were then grown on, and those which proved to be fixed in all recognisable features were multiplied as rapidly as possible with the object of carrying out baking trials. These tests made on the $F_4$ generation of the cross showed that the endosperm of the grain was either that of one parent or the other and that it was never a blend of both. We had then for the first time proof that the wheat breeder could definitely undertake to build up varieties possessing this characteristic hitherto unknown amongst English wheats. But, simple as it may appear to put this knowledge to practical use, many difficulties have been met with in the attempts to do so. Chief amongst these is the fact that in the $F_2$ generations from many Fife hybrids the segregation into strong and weak cannot be recognised with any approach to the certainty with which it could be in the case first investigated. This is due to the fact that even English wheat may have all the appearance of a strong wheat, though in the bakehouse it may be impossible to make a presentable loaf from it. One can control this appearance to a certain extent by appropriate cultural conditions, but still the fact remains that one has to work with characteristics which one cannot readily identify. Under these circumstances part of the produce of every plant chosen for further propagation has to be tested by the tedious chewing process or one has to chance matters and trust that the $F_3$ or $F_4$ generation will reveal the characteristics with greater certainty. The method, though satisfactory in practice, is far from ideal, for it involves the use of a considerable area of land and a great deal of labour at harvest time when it can least be spared. The next difficulty is to secure the combination of strength and high yield in one and the same variety, for the strong wheats we have to use as parents for the time being cannot be said to be average croppers except under particularly favourable conditions. This combination is essential because heaviness of crop outweighs every other consideration with the English farmer, though in countries such as Canada quality is the chief factor which determines whether or not a variety is worth cultivating. Unfortunately very little is known

# YIELDING CAPACITY OF WHEAT

with regard to the factors which determine the yield per acre. Many play their part in determining it, the master factor of the whole set probably being the available water supply during the period of most rapid growth in May and June. If this is suitable then soils usually considered unsuitable for wheat cultivation can carry crops well up to the general average of the country. Apart from this, however, yield is largely a matter of variety, for on the same field one variety may consistently give greater crops than another. Whether the capacities for giving large or small yields are hereditary or not has so far proved incapable of analysis. There is evidence that such segregation can occur, for high and low yielding varieties have been isolated from the same cross when there has been an appreciable difference in these respects in the parents. But to estimate the proportions of the two forms in the $F_2$ generations is impossible, for no inspection of a single plant can reveal its cropping capacity per acre. In handling crosses between low-yielding strong wheats and heavy-yielding weak wheats much has to be left to chance. One simply picks out the types one considers suitable and then after rejecting those which are obviously deficient in strength propagates them with a view to determining their cropping capacity as opportunity offers. For selecting in this fashion it is essential that the plants of the $F_2$ generation should be grown under the

## 172 SYSTEMATIZED PLANT-BREEDING

most uniform conditions possible. Otherwise the favoured plants would undoubtedly be chosen as starting points of the new varieties. Fortunately this is easily effected by a system of uniform spacing between the plants. As the germination of the grain is usually from 95 to 100 per cent. blanks, and consequently favoured plants, do not occur frequently.

The ordinary method of testing the yield per acre is to grow plots of an acre or so alongside similar plots of some standard variety. The actual yields of grain and straw are then compared directly. The method is not satisfactory, for the margin of error even under good experimental conditions may amount to five per cent., and where a real difference of two or three per cent. is too valuable to be missed it is folly to attempt to use it even if the expense of testing large numbers of varieties in this way could be faced. The method now in use consists of growing small plots under the most uniform soil conditions obtainable, each variety under trial being represented by a minimum of twenty plots. These are four feet square with the rows six inches apart and the plants two inches apart in the rows. At harvest the central square yard of each plot is gathered plant by plant and notes made of the number of plants surviving and the number of ears they bear. These figures give the number of tillers per plant—a feature of great importance

## YIELD AND STRENGTH

in estimating the possibilities of yield. Later on the yield of grain from each plot is ascertained and a simple calculation enables one to compare all the varieties under trial. The margin of error rarely exceeds two per cent. and under favourable conditions it is considerably less. The data so obtained together with the more inaccurate but at the same time highly essential personal judgments as to the suitability of the varieties for general cultivation enable one to decide whether tests on the wholesale scale are desirable.

Up to the present only one variety showing the combination of yield and strength has been tested on the commercial scale. This is one known as Burgoyne's Fife, the name commemorating the fact that it was raised on the Burgoyne's farm lent to the University Department of Agriculture by Mr W. A. Macfarlane Grieve of Impington. It was one of the many forms isolated from the cross between Rough Chaff (an old English wheat rarely grown now) and Red Fife already described. The Red Fife parent was chosen at hazard from a small crop grown from ordinary commercial seed at a time when it was not known that individual plants of Red Fife vary a little in the quality of their grain and we had not isolated the pure lines we now have. In consequence we do not know whether the parent plant possessed the strength of Red Fife at its best. The hybrid does not, but resembles in both the mill and the bakehouse a strain since isolated from Red Fife. Whatever the actual position of affairs is Burgoyne's Fife proved in the baking trials to be so superior to any English wheat that on the recommendation of the Home-grown Wheat Committee it was introduced into commerce. In one respect it has been disappointing, for it has proved to be uncertain in its cropping capacity, a feature it may possibly have inherited from either of its parents. But on lands suitable for its cultivation its yield per acre is well up to the average. Where this is the case it is grown on a large scale and its grain takes the place of imported strong wheats in the local mills. The fact is of interest, for Burgoyne's Fife is a white grained wheat and it was generally believed amongst millers that strength was only found in association with coloured wheats. The recognition of the incorrectness of this view simplifies the work of breeding new strong types, for lack of colour is a recessive character and consequently one is not concerned with the necessity of determining whether it is "fixed." From the milling point of view too the information was welcome, for highly developed as the modern rolling processes are the grain coats are still slightly powdered during the earlier crushings, with the result that the flour is slightly discoloured if they are at all dark. This variety has inherited from Red Fife its habit of rapid maturation and consequently it can be sown as a spring wheat. During the

## THE POSSIBILITIES OF MENDELISM

past two seasons when it has been necessary to extend the cultivation of wheat as much as possible it has been largely used for this purpose. Of the newer varieties in which strength and high yield are combined little can be said at present since they have not been tested on the commercial scale. We know that on the experimental farm they easily outcrop Square Head's Master, the standard wheat of the country, whilst they stand better under adverse climatic circumstances. They are now being multiplied as rapidly as possible with the view of bringing them into general cultivation in the hope that they may play some part in making wheat-growing here a more profitable industry and so lead to an extension of our home-grown food supplies.

But the end of the work is not in sight yet. Several other possibilities of improving the crop still remain, and one can now look forward to carrying the work through with a fair degree of certainty, for we have measured the possibilities of using Mendel's principles from the economic standpoint and know that once there is proof of the independent inheritance of any character then it can be worked up into any combinations one requires.

# AN AGRICULTURAL WAR PROBLEM

By T. B. WOOD, M.A.

*Drapers Professor of Agriculture in the University of Cambridge.*

The following pages attempt to describe how the staff of the Cambridge School of Agriculture have tried to solve a problem submitted to them at the beginning of 1915 by the President of the Board of Agriculture and Fisheries. The problem, like most matters claiming the attention of the country at the present time, arose out of the war. Farmers as a body have never taken a serious interest in the scientific principles upon which the practice of the feeding of animals is based. Perhaps they have been justified, to some extent, in this course, for two reasons: in the first place most of the data on which the science of the nutrition of farm animals rests have been drawn from German or American sources, and the conclusions based on them are not applicable with absolute strictness to British conditions and British fodders. In the second place the actual number of different fodders generally used by farmers is so small that they have felt that they could rely on rule of thumb knowledge gained by their own past experience. Home-grown hay, straw, and roots provide the bulk of the fodder they require, and their purchases are practically confined to linseed cake, cotton cake, maize and wheat offals. These few items, together with a few home-grown oats for their horses and tail corn for their poultry and pigs, practically exhaust the list of feeding stuffs used by the great body of farmers.

As long as prices remained about constant, or altered slowly and regularly, rule-of-thumb knowledge of the value and general properties of the few feeding stuffs mentioned above sufficed to enable farmers to produce meat, milk, and work with some kind of success, though their practice included many instances of ignorant wastefulness. But when the war introduced new conditions and prices of feeding stuffs rose suddenly and irregularly by from 30 to 100 per cent., rule-of-thumb knowledge entirely failed to meet the emergency. Practical experience could not show farmers how to buy, and still less how to use, feeding stuffs which they had never seen before.

Although many feeding stuffs, which before the war went to Germany, were forced on to British markets at comparatively low prices, farmers, from lack of knowledge of their value and properties, were compelled to adhere to their old-accustomed linseed cake, cotton cake, maize and wheat offals, which soon rose to prices at which their use prohibited all chance of profitable stock-keeping. This was the state of things when in February, 1915, Lord Selborne suggested that the staff of the School of Agriculture should endeavour to show the farmers how to buy and use the newer and cheaper feeding stuffs to the best advantage. The President no doubt addressed his suggestion to Cambridge because his Board had established, in connection with the School of Agriculture, by means of a grant from the Development Fund, an Institute for Research in Animal Nutrition. The staff of the Institute were requested to undertake the work, and in doing so they have received the hearty cooperation of their colleagues on the staff of the School of Agriculture.

The President offered to supply at the end of each month a list of quotations of the prices of all the feeding stuffs on the great wholesale markets of London, Liverpool, Hull and Bristol, and suggested that a report should be prepared showing in some simple manner the relative cost of the nutrients in all these feeding stuffs so as to guide the farmers in buying. It was also suggested that the report should include rations in which the new feeding stuffs were included in order to show the farmers how to use them. The first report was published by the Board of Agriculture in their Journal for March, 1915. Reports on similar lines have appeared in each succeeding monthly issue of the Journal under the title of "Notes on Feeding Stuffs." As a result of the appearance of the "Notes" members of the staff have been asked to confer with farmers' clubs in order to give further information about the newer kinds of feeding stuffs. A large amount of correspondence on the subject has been received and answered. The newer feeding stuffs which were recommended as suitable for British conditions have been used largely and successfully, and their use has certainly helped farmers to produce meat and milk under very difficult conditions.

The story of the problem has now been told, but the real interest lies not in the story itself but in the method of solution. As presented by the President the problem consisted of two separate parts: how to buy feeding stuffs to the best advantage, and how to use them when bought. Feeding stuffs are offered on the markets at prices per ton, per quarter, or per bushel. The Board were good enough to send the quotations to Cambridge worked out uniformly at prices per ton. But price per ton is not a reliable criterion of feeding value, for different feeding stuffs contain different proportions of nutrients. The first step was to compile a table showing the percentage of the various nutrients in all the feeding stuffs on the markets. This was not quite a simple matter, because most of the tables of analyses given in the books dealing with foods were made from German fodders. However, after a considerable search through the literature a fairly satisfactory table based on British analyses was compiled.

An ordinary analysis however is not a reliable measure of relative feeding value, for fodders differ greatly in digestibility. Thus of the total amount of nutrients shown by analysis to be present in linseed cake about 90 per cent. is digestible, whilst in hay the digestible nutrients do not amount to much more than half the total nutrients indicated by an ordinary analysis. A determination of the digestible nutrients in a sample of a feeding stuff is a lengthy and not very pleasant process, involving the collection and analysis of the whole of the solid excreta of an animal for a period of about 10 days, whilst he eats a known weight of the food. Information is fortunately on record as to the digestibility of almost every known feeding stuff. For instance it is known that of the protein of linseed cake 86 per cent. is digestible, of the fat 90 per cent., of the carbohydrates 80 per cent. and of the fibre 50 per cent. Similar figures are available for almost every kind of feeding stuff. From these figures and the table of the average composition of the feeding stuffs on the home markets it was possible to calculate Table I which shows the percentages of digestible nutrients in all the feeding stuffs included in the quotations collected by the Board of Agriculture.

It will at once occur to anyone acquainted

## Table I.

| Name of feeding stuff | Percentage of digestible nutrients ||| Food units per ton |
|---|---|---|---|---|
| | Protein | Fat | Carbohydrates and fibre | |
| *Foods Rich in both Protein and Oil or Fat* | | | | |
| Ground-nut cake ... | 45·2 | 6·3 | 21·1 | 145 |
| Soya bean cake ... | 34·0 | 6·5 | 21·0 | 122 |
| Decort. cotton cake ... | 34·0 | 8·5 | 20·0 | 126 |
| Linseed cake, Indian ... | 27·8 | 9·3 | 30·1 | 123 |
| Linseed cake, English ... | 26·7 | 9·3 | 30·1 | 120 |
| Cotton cake, Egyptian | 15·5 | 5·3 | 20·0 | 72 |
| Cotton cake, Bombay ... | 13·1 | 4·4 | 21·5 | 65 |
| Distillers' grains ... | 18·7 | 10·2 | 29·0 | 101 |
| Maize gluten feed ... | 20·4 | 8·8 | 48·4 | 122 |
| Brewers' grains, dried ... | 14·1 | 6·6 | 32·7 | 85 |
| Coconut cake ... ... | 16·3 | 8·2 | 41·4 | 103 |
| Palm-nut kernel cake ... | 12·5 | 7·7 | 39·0 | 91 |
| Linseed ... ... ... | 18·1 | 34·7 | 20·1 | 154 |
| Bombay cotton seed ... | 11·0 | 16·8 | 30·1 | 100 |
| *Fairly Rich in Protein, Rich in Oil* | | | | |
| Maize germ meal ... | 9·0 | 6·2 | 61·2 | 99 |
| Rice meal ... ... | 6·8 | 10·2 | 38·2 | 79 |
| *Rich in Protein, Poor in Oil* | | | | |
| Peas, Calcutta white ... | 23·3 | 1·1 | 45·9 | 98 |
| Beans, English ... ... | 19·3 | 1·2 | 48·2 | 100 |
| Beans, Chinese ... ... | 19·6 | 1·7 | 47·9 | 101 |
| Peas, English maple ... | 17·0 | 1·0 | 50·0 | 97 |
| Brewers' grains, wet ... | 3·5 | 1·5 | 8·6 | 21 |
| Malt culms ... ... | 11·4 | 1·1 | 38·6 | 70 |
| *Cereals, Rich in Starch, not Rich in Protein or Oil* | | | | |
| Barley, feeding ... ... | 8·0 | 2·1 | 57·8 | 83 |
| Oats, English ... ... | 7·2 | 4·0 | 47·4 | 75 |
| Oats, Argentine ... ... | 7·2 | 4·0 | 47·4 | 75 |
| Maize, American ... | 6·7 | 4·5 | 65·8 | 94 |
| Maize, Argentine ... | 6·8 | 4·5 | 65·8 | 94 |
| Maize meal ... ... | 5·5 | 3·5 | 63·9 | 87 |
| Wheat middlings ... | 12·0 | 3·0 | 56·0 | 93 |
| Wheat sharps ... ... | 12·0 | 4·0 | 50·0 | 86 |
| Wheat pollards ... ... | 11·6 | 3·5 | 53·0 | 82 |
| Wheat bran ... ... | 11·3 | 3·0 | 45·0 | 76 |
| Wheat bran, broad ... | 11·3 | 3·0 | 45·4 | 80 |

with the feeding-stuff market that the list includes only those feeding stuffs which are made of one article, all compound feeding stuffs being omitted. This perhaps requires a word of explanation. The reason is that feeding stuffs made from only one article have a more or less standard composition which never differs widely from the average. It is therefore possible to give their average composition with a fair measure of certainty, so that any sample which a farmer may buy will not differ appreciably from the figures given. But compound feeding stuffs are made of a mixture of various articles in varying proportions, both the constituents and the proportions in which they are mixed varying according to the markets. The only constant property they possess is the presence of some condimental ingredient which is incorporated in order to produce a scent and flavour which makes them palatable. They are not likely to possess a reasonably constant composition or digestibility and it is therefore impossible to state their average content of digestible nutrients with any degree of certainty so that the figures would correctly represent the samples on the market.

Before the figures in the table can be used as a guide for buying it is necessary to reduce them to one denomination. In the case of fat, carbohydrates, and fibre, this is readily done, for digestible carbohydrates and digestible fibre are equivalent to one another, and 1 lb. of digestible fat

# FOOD UNITS

has been proved experimentally to be equivalent to about 2½ lbs. of either of them. But it is not so easy to reduce protein to its carbohydrate equivalent, for its function is to repair the waste of the working parts of the body, whilst fats, carbohydrates and fibre act as fuel. It is indeed impossible to compare the value of protein with that of other nutrients on a scientific basis, for the function of protein is quite distinct. But for the purpose of comparing values on the market, protein may be reduced to its carbohydrate equivalent on a money basis, when it is found that the average price of 1 lb. of protein is 2½ times as much as the average price of 1 lb. of carbohydrate. By adding together the percentages of protein and fat, multiplying the sum by 2½, and then adding to the result the percentages of digestible carbohydrate and fibre, a figure is obtained which represents the amount of carbohydrates equivalent in money value to the whole of the nutrients of the feeding stuff. Taking as the unit for this purpose one-hundredth of a ton of carbohydrates, the figure represents the number of food units equivalent to all the digestible nutrients in a ton of the food. The cost per food unit can then be calculated simply by dividing the price per ton by the number of food units. In this manner the cost per food unit of all the feeding stuffs included in the quotations has been calculated, and is given in Table II. The cost per food unit varies from

## TABLE II.

| Name of feeding stuff | April 1915 s. d. | May 1916 s. d. |
|---|---|---|
| Ground-nut cake | — | 1  6¼ |
| Brewers' grains, wet | 1  1½ | 1  6¾ |
| Maize gluten feed | 1  4½ | 1  10¼ |
| Soya bean cake | 1  4½ | 1  9½ |
| Coconut cake | 1  5½ | 1  11¾ |
| Wheat middlings | 1  5½ | 2  1 |
| Decorticated cotton cake | 1  6 | 2  0¾ |
| Palm-nut kernel cake | 1  7 | 1  9¼ |
| Brewers' grains, dried | 1  7½ | 2  0½ |
| Wheat sharps | 1  7½ | 2  2¼ |
| Malt culms | 1  7½ | 2  2¾ |
| Maize germ meal | 1  8½ | 2  5¼ |
| Maize, Argentine | 1  9 | 2  7 |
| Linseed cake, Indian | 1  9 | 1  10½ |
| Rice meal, Egyptian | 1  9 | 2  6¼ |
| Wheat bran | 1  9 | 1  11¼ |
| Rice meal, Burmese | 1  9½ | 2  4¼ |
| Maize, American | 1  10 | 2  7¼ |
| Linseed cake, English | 1  10 | 1  11¼ |
| Wheat bran, broad | 1  10½ | 2  1¾ |
| Cotton cake, Egyptian | 1  11 | 2  8 |
| Beans, English | 1  11 | 2  5¾ |
| Cotton cake, Bombay | 2  0 | 2  7½ |
| Maize meal | 2  0½ | 2  10¼ |
| Beans, Chinese | 2  1½ | 2  4¼ |
| Barley, English feeding | 2  3 | 3  5¼ |
| Peas, English dun | 2  4½ | 2  7¼ |
| Peas, English maple | 2  9½ | 2  9¾ |
| Oats, Argentine | 2  11½ | 3  2½ |
| Peas, Calcutta white | 3  0 | 3  9½ |
| Oats, English | 3  1 | 3  2½ |

## COST PER FOOD UNIT

1s. 6¼d. in ground-nut cake to 3s. 2½d. in English oats, a range which gives plenty of scope for economy.

The price per food unit is a reliable basis for comparing the price of various feeding stuffs on the market, but it is by no means the whole story. When a farmer goes to market to buy feeding stuffs he usually has some definite purpose in mind. He intends for instance to buy some kind of concentrated food to supplement the home-grown fodders he has grown for his fattening bullocks or milking cows. He knows by experience that a concentrated food with astringent properties is required to make a successful diet along with the large amount of succulent fodder provided by his roots, and he consequently buys cotton cake, or a mixture of cotton cake and linseed cake. He knows that by adjusting the relative proportions of linseed cake, which is laxative, with cotton cake, which is astringent, he can keep the digestive organs of his stock in proper condition all the year round whether the rest of their ration is dry food in the winter or luscious grass in the early summer.

Farmers have learned by experience the practical properties of the foods they have been accustomed to use, but it was necessary to find out the properties of the new foods before they could be recommended for general use, and to point out that although the food unit system is an excellent aid to comparing the prices of different foods, it must be used under definite limitations. The food to buy is not necessarily that which is cheapest per food unit, but that which is cheapest per food unit and at the same time suitable for the purpose for which it is required. Fortunately a certain amount of information as to the general properties of many of the new foods was available from feeding trials made on the University Farm, at the Norfolk Agricultural Station, and at many of the Agricultural Colleges. This was supplemented by a study of the agricultural literature of Germany where the new foods had been in general use for some time. Altogether sufficient information was collected to enable the staff to compile rations in which many of the new foods were included. Further information has since come to hand through the courtesy of numerous correspondents who have tried the rations which were recommended.

An illustration of the method used in framing a ration will explain the points just discussed.

Table II gives the cost per food unit of about 30 foods on the markets in April, 1915. Oats were at that date the most expensive food on the market, English oats costing 3s. 1d. per food unit and Argentine oats 2s. 11½d. Farmers are accustomed to use oats for their horses, but to continue to do so at these prices was not only extravagant but also most unpatriotic, for the oats were required for the Army horses.

## SUBSTITUTE FOR OATS

It was therefore necessary to compile a mixture to replace oats. Looking down the list of prices in Table II the first six foods are found for various reasons to be unsuitable for the purpose. Dried brewers' grains, the seventh in order of cheapness, was little used in Great Britain before the war. The Norfolk Experiments had shown that it was useful for fattening sheep. German literature recorded its successful use for horses as a constituent of a mixed ration. The next food in order of cheapness per food unit, wheat sharps, is too soft and finely ground to use alone, but goes well with bran which is very slightly dearer. Rice meal when mixed with other things was also known by experience to suit horses. It was decided to recommend a mixture of these four foods in such proportions as would approximate in composition to oats, namely dried grains 6 lb., wheat sharps 2 lb., bran 4 lb. and rice meal 2 lb. Such a mixture could be prepared at 1s. $8\frac{1}{4}d.$ per food unit and its use would effect a saving of about 6d. per day per horse.

It proved quite satisfactory for farm horses which are only called upon to do slow work. It could not be used in place of oats for Army horses which may be required to do rapid work at short notice.

It may not be clear from the explanation given above why it was thought advisable to recommend a mixture of four foods rather than one food only. This raises an interesting and important point on which the staff of the Cambridge Nutrition Institute have been working for some time. It has already been stated that every animal requires daily a certain amount of protein to make good the wear and tear of its working parts, or tissues as they are called. Twenty years ago physiologists would have been satisfied with this statement. But recent work on the chemistry of the proteins has shown the need for caution in applying definite standards for protein requirements. The protein of wheat for instance has been shown to yield on digestion something like 40 per cent. of one constituent called glutaminic acid. This particular constituent is not required in large quantities by animals. If an animal is given all its protein in the form of wheat it will require more than the standard amount of protein, for much of the glutaminic acid of the wheat protein will be in excess of the animal's requirements for that substance and will go to waste. The animal will be able to repair its tissue waste with a smaller amount of protein if part of it is given in the form of a protein which contains a smaller proportion of glutaminic acid and consequently more of the other protein constituents. Unfortunately our knowledge of the constituents of the proteins of many fodders is far from complete, but there is a much better chance of getting a mixture of constituents proportionate to the needs of the animal if a mixed ration is given than if the animal is fed on one food only.

## MANURIAL VALUE

In the absence of definite knowledge of the constitution of the proteins of most fodders the safe course is to recommend a mixed ration.

Having framed such a mixed ration the next step is to decide in what quantity it is to be used. At first sight it might appear that foods should be used in proportion to the number of food units they contain, but a little consideration shows that food units are not a measure of nutritive value, for in calculating them the factor for reducing protein to its carbohydrate equivalent was avowedly based on market prices which are certainly not related to nutritive value.

The market price of protein is high because protein contains nitrogen and phosphorus which have manurial as well as nutritive value. The protein repairs the animal's tissues but is not retained permanently in the body. Nearly the whole of its nitrogen and phosphorus is excreted and raises the value of the farm-yard manure produced by the stock. The manurial value is a considerable item in the market price. In the case of linseed cake costing before the war £9 per ton the manurial value was assessed at about £2 per ton. Manurial value is not related directly to nutritive value and, being included in the calculation of food units, food units cannot be used as a guide in arranging a ration.

For arranging rations it was necessary to consider two points: the relative proportion of protein in the foods which it was proposed to use, and the total nutritive value of the foods. The relative proportion of protein was expressed by reducing the fat to its carbohydrate equivalent as before by multiplying the percentage of digestible fat by $2\frac{1}{2}$. The product was then added to the percentages of digestible carbohydrates and fibre, and the sum divided by the percentage of digestible protein. This gave the ratio of protein to fats, carbohydrates and fibre all reduced to carbohydrate equivalent. It was stated in the form of the ratio of 1 part of protein to so many parts of non-protein food, and appears in Table IV (p. 199) under the well-known name, nutritive ratio. In replacing one food by another, or one mixture by another, it is necessary to preserve approximately the same nutritive ratio. For instance if it is desired to replace a mixture of linseed cake and cotton cake, which have become very expensive, by ground nut cake, which is still comparatively cheap, the ground nut cake must be, so to speak, diluted with something with a wide nutritive ratio so that the nutritive ratio of the mixture may be approximately that of the mixture of linseed and cotton cakes.

The question of total nutritive value is not quite so simple. Many attempts have been made to reduce all the constituents of a food to one common denomination so that the total nutritive value of the food may be expressed by one figure, which is commonly called the starch equivalent.

## STARCH EQUIVALENTS

Two of these methods have been employed in "monthly notes" in assessing the starch equivalent of foods, the first based on calculation from the nett heat value to the animal of the various nutrients contained in the food, the second purely experimental. The nett heat values of the various nutrients have been ascertained experimentally by means of the respiration calorimeter, a complicated apparatus which enables the experimenter to feed an animal as large as an ox on a weighed and analysed diet, to collect, weigh and analyse the whole of his excreta both solid, liquid and gaseous, and to measure the amount of heat he gives out. By means of this apparatus it has been found that the nett heat values of the nutrients digested by an animal such as an ox are as follows:

TABLE III.

|  | Nett heat value to animal ||  Nett heat value, carbohydrate $= 1$ |
|---|---|---|---|
|  | per gram. | per lb. |  |
| Protein | 4·70 cal. | 2134 cal. | 1·25 |
| Fat | 8·80 ,, | 4000 ,, | 2·34 |
| Carbohydrates or fibre | 3·76 ,, | 1700 ,, | 1·00 |

These values are the nett values realized in the animal's body. They differ from the amount of heat given out when nutrients are burned outside the body. For instance the heat of combustion of protein per gram is 5·80 cal. The difference between this figure and the nett value of 4·70 cal. is due to the fact that when protein is burned outside the body it is burned completely, but when it is oxidized in the body the oxidation is not complete, only proceeding as far as urea, uric acid, hippuric acid and similar compounds. The difference between the gross heat of combustion of 5·80 cal. and the nett heat value of 4·70 cal. is the heat value left in these incompletely oxidized compounds. The animal is able to obtain practically the whole of the heat value of the fats in its food: the gross heat of combustion and the nett heat value to the animal are the same. Carbohydrates are subject to fermentation in the digestive organs of the animal. Marsh gas and similar products are produced and cause a loss of about 10 per cent. of the heat value of these nutrients. The difference between the gross heat of combustion of carbohydrates, 4·10 cal. per gram, and the nett value to the animal, 3·76 cal. per gram, is due to this cause. The last column in Table III gives the relative nett heat values to the animal of proteins and fats, the nett value of carbohydrates being taken as unity.

From these figures it is possible to calculate the starch equivalent of any food from its content of digestible nutrients. Thus the starch equivalent will be the sum of the percentage of digestible

## MAINTENANCE

protein multiplied by 1·25, digestible fat multiplied by 2·34, digestible carbohydrates and digestible fibre.

This will give the amount of starch, or similar carbohydrate, equivalent in nett heat value to the animal to 100 lb. of the food.

But the experiments by which were determined the nett heat values on which this calculation is based were all made on animals kept on a diet which was only sufficient to keep their weight constant. Such a diet is known as a maintenance ration, and starch equivalents calculated in this way should be called maintenance starch equivalents.

The reason for using this distinctive name becomes apparent when the purely experimental method of finding starch equivalents is considered. This method is due to Kellner who proceeded as follows. An ox was kept in a respiration chamber so that his total excreta, solid, liquid and gaseous, could be collected, weighed and analysed. His diet was then adjusted so as to maintain him at constant weight. The diet was exactly weighed and analysed. It was then increased by the addition of 1000 grams of starch per day, when the weight of the animal was found to increase.

Comparison of the weight of carbon in the food with the weight of carbon in the excreta showed that the increase was due chiefly to storage of something containing a high percentage of carbon.

This could only be fat. Since fat contains 76 per cent. of carbon, the amount of fat stored could be calculated from the difference between the carbon in the food and the carbon in the excreta. This figure was not quite exact, since comparison of the nitrogen in the food and in the excreta showed that a trace of protein was also stored, which must contain a trace of carbon. This could easily be allowed for, since protein contains 16 per cent. of nitrogen and 53 per cent. of carbon. Having applied this correction it was found that the addition of 1000 grams of starch to the maintenance diet caused the production in the body of 250 grams of fat.

The animal was now placed once more on his maintenance ration and after an interval this was increased by the addition of 1000 grams of some other food, say linseed cake. Applying the same methods it was found that 1000 grams of linseed cake caused the production in the body of 192 grams of fat.

From these results the starch equivalent of 100 lb. of linseed cake for fat production is evidently $100 \times 192 \div 250$, or 77 lb. of starch.

Experiments of this kind are extraordinarily troublesome and very expensive. Nevertheless Kellner was able to carry through enough of them to enable him to assign starch equivalents to some 300 foods. These were not all based directly on separate experiments, but the experiments carried through provided a basis for calculation. It was

# FAT PRODUCTION

shown for instance that 1000 grams of protein added to a maintenance ration caused 235 grams of fat to be produced in the body. The value of protein for fat production is therefore $235 \div 250$ or ·94 that of starch. Similarly it was found that the value of fat for fat production compared with the value of starch for fat production was 2·4 in the case of the fat of oil cakes, 2·2 for the fat of cereals, and 1·9 for the fat of coarse fodders such as hay or straw. By means of these figures the starch equivalent for fat production of any food could be calculated. But when the figure calculated in this manner was compared with the figure found by direct experiment on the lines described above for linseed cake, the calculated starch equivalent was almost always found to exceed the starch equivalent experimentally determined. Thus in the case of linseed cake the starch equivalent calculated from the digestible nutrients by applying Kellner's relative values for fat production gave the following result:

|  | lb. starch equivalent |
|---|---|
| 27·0 per cent. digestible protein × 0·94 | = 25·38 |
| 9·3 per cent. digestible fat × 2·4 | = 22·32 |
| 26·2 per cent. digestible carbohydrate + 4·5 per cent. digestible fibre | = 30·70 |
| 100 lbs. linseed cake | = 78·40 |

Since 1000 grams of starch had been shown by direct experiment to cause the production of 250

## 196 AN AGRICULTURAL WAR PROBLEM

grams of fat, 1000 grams of linseed cake having this starch equivalent should cause the production of 196 grams of fat. Direct experiment however showed that 1000 grams of this particular linseed cake produced only 192 grams of fat, or 98 per cent. of the amount which it ought to have produced if the calculated starch equivalent were really exact. The true starch equivalent was then calculated from the calculated starch equivalent by multiplying the latter by $98 \div 100$. This figure 98 which gives the ratio of the true starch equivalent to the calculated starch equivalent was called by Kellner the value number. It expresses the ratio of the true starch equivalent to the starch equivalent calculated from the percentage of digestible nutrients by Kellner's method. Kellner determined the value numbers for all the different classes of foods. By the aid of these and the values of the separate digestible nutrients he was able to assign starch equivalents to all the 300 foods included in the list he gives in his book. For instance the starch equivalent of average meadow hay was calculated thus:

|  | Digestible nutrients per cent. |  |  |
|---|---|---|---|
| Protein | 4·6 × 0·94 | = | 4·32 |
| Fat | 0·6 × 1·90 | = | 1·14 |
| Carbohydrates | 21·1 × 1·0 | = | 21·10 |
| Fibre | 15·3 × 1·0 | = | 15·30 |
|  |  |  | 41·86 |

## FAT PRODUCTION

The value number for hay is 58, and the true starch equivalent therefore $41 \cdot 86 \times 58 \div 100 = 24$. This figure means that 100 lb. of average meadow hay may be expected to produce as much fat as would be produced by 24 lb. of starch. Kellner's value numbers vary from 100 for very easily digested foods to 30 for such foods as straw which are digested with difficulty. The need for them arises from the fact that in the case of easily digested foods practically the whole of the digestible nutrients are available for fat production, whilst in the case of such foods as straw 70 per cent. of the energy of the nutrients is used up in the processes of mastication and digestion and only 30 per cent. is left over for fat production.

It is interesting to note that the value number for articles like sawdust is a minus quantity, which means that when such articles were added to a maintenance diet the energy required for their mastication and digestion exceeded the energy of the digestible nutrients they contain. These were in fact digested at the expense of the energy of the rest of the food and the animal to which they were given decreased in weight instead of storing fat.

Starch equivalents determined by Kellner's method are intended to measure the relative value of different foods for fat production. They should therefore be called production starch equivalents, and they may be used as an index of value for production generally not only of fat, but of growth, milk, or work.

Table IV gives side by side the maintenance and production starch equivalents of the foods which have been on the market since the war began. For comparison a few coarse fodders have been included. It will be noticed that for coarse fodders the maintenance starch equivalents greatly exceed the production starch equivalents. Such fodders, hay, straw and the like should therefore be used for maintenance, that is to say for maintaining the temperature and vital functions. If an animal is required to produce anything, fat, meat, growth, milk or work, its diet should be increased by addition of some suitable concentrated food of which the greater part of the digestible nutrients are available for production.

The object of the monthly notes was to show the farmer how to buy and use unaccustomed foods. It has been explained how the food unit method of comparing values helped him to buy foods. It must now be explained how Table IV has helped him in using foods. This is perhaps best done by an example. A standard ration for fattening bullocks largely used by farmers is:

Two bushels of swede turnips, weighing about 84 lb., 10 lb. of straw, and 4 lb. of a mixture of linseed and cotton cakes, rising to 8 lb. as fattening proceeds.

During last winter linseed and cotton cakes

## Table IV.

| Name of feeding stuff | Nutritive ratio | Production Starch equiv. per 100 lb. | Maintenance Starch equiv. per 100 lb. |
|---|---|---|---|
| *Foods Rich in both Protein and Oil or Fat* | | | |
| Ground-nut cake | 1 : 0·8 | 77·5 | 92 |
| Soya bean cake | 1 : 1·1 | 66·7 | 79 |
| Decort. cotton cake | 1 : 1·2 | 71·0 | 82 |
| Linseed cake, Indian | 1 : 1·9 | 77·1 | 87 |
| Linseed cake, English | 1 : 2·0 | 76·0 | 85 |
| Cotton cake, Egyptian | 1 : 2·1 | 40·0 | 52 |
| Cotton cake, Bombay | 1 : 2·5 | 37·6 | 48 |
| Distillers' grains | 1 : 2·9 | 57·3 | 76 |
| Maize gluten feed | 1 : 3·0 | 87·4 | 94 |
| Brewers' grains, dried | 1 : 3·5 | 50·3 | 65 |
| Coconut cake | 1 : 3·8 | 76·5 | 81 |
| Palm-nut kernel cake | 1 : 4·6 | 69·5 | 73 |
| Linseed | 1 : 5·9 | 119·2 | 124 |
| Bombay cotton seed | 1 : 6·6 | 77·5 | 83 |
| *Fairly Rich in Protein, Rich in Oil* | | | |
| Maize germ meal | 1 : 8·5 | 81·0 | 87 |
| Rice meal | 1 : 9·4 | 68·4 | 71 |
| *Rich in Protein, Poor in Oil* | | | |
| Peas, Calcutta white | 1 : 2·1 | 66·9 | 78 |
| Beans, English | 1 : 2·6 | 67·0 | 75 |
| Peas, English maple | 1 : 3·1 | 70·0 | 73 |
| Brewers' grains, wet | 1 : 3·5 | 12·7 | 16 |
| Malt culms | 1 : 3·6 | 38·7 | 55 |
| *Cereals, Rich in Starch, not Rich in Protein or Oil* | | | |
| Barley, feeding | 1 : 8·0 | 67·9 | 73 |
| Oats, English | 1 : 8·0 | 59·7 | 66 |
| Maize, American | 1 : 11·5 | 81·0 | 85 |
| Maize, Argentine | 1 : 11·3 | 83·5 | 86 |
| Maize meal | 1 : 13·0 | 77·8 | 79 |
| Wheat middlings | 1 : 5·3 | 59·1 | 78 |
| Wheat sharps | 1 : 5·0 | 58·4 | 74 |
| Wheat pollards | 1 : 5·3 | 54·1 | 78 |
| Wheat bran | 1 : 4·7 | 49·7 | 66 |
| *Coarse Fodders* | | | |
| Meadow hay, good | 1 : 11·3 | 31·0 | 49 |
| ,,   ,,   poor | 1 : 14·4 | 19·0 | 40 |
| Oat straw | 1 : 54·0 | 22·0 | 41 |

were so dear that to use them precluded all chance of profitable beef production.  Ground-nut cake was far the cheapest food on the market suitable for the purpose.  But ground-nut cake has too narrow a nutritive ratio, 1 : 0·8, to replace linseed and cotton cake without the addition of something to dilute its too high protein content.  All foods rich in carbohydrates with wide nutritive ratios were extremely dear to buy, but swede turnips were plentiful, and being home grown might be considered cheap.  They contain a large proportion of carbohydrate and practically no protein, so farmers were recommended to use ground-nut cake and to dilute its excess of protein by increasing the ration of swedes.  In order to assess the ration the following procedure was adopted.  Table I shows that 4 lb. of a mixture of linseed and cotton cakes contains ·84 lb. of digestible protein and 2·32 lb. of starch equivalent.  As swedes contain practically no protein, it will be necessary to give all the protein in the form of ground-nut cake.  Reference to Table I once more shows that 2 lb. of ground-nut cake contains ·90 lb. of digestible protein, which is near enough to ·84 lb.  The starch equivalent of 2 lb. of ground-nut cake is 1·55 lb.  This leaves 2·32 minus 1·55, *i.e.* ·77 lb. of starch equivalent to be supplied by the addition of swede turnips.  Since the starch equivalent of 100 lb. of swede turnips is 7 lb., the weight required to supply ·77 lb. of starch equivalent is 11 lb. of swede turnips.  The

4 lb. of mixed linseed and cotton cakes, costing last autumn $4\frac{1}{4}d.$, could be replaced by 2 lb. of ground-nut cake costing $2d.$, and 11 lb. of swede turnips costing about $\frac{1}{2}d.$ This resulted in a saving of $1\frac{3}{4}d.$ per day on each bullock, which would increase as the ration was raised and fattening proceeded. The total saving would have amounted to about $25s.$ on each bullock fattened.

If the writer has succeded in his object, it will be realized that in many branches of the science of nutrition our knowledge is sufficiently exact to enable us to assist the farmer in feeding his animals with benefit to his pocket and ultimate profit to the nation.

But in our knowledge there are many gaps, some of which the staff of the Institute were attempting to fill when the war interrupted their work. Perhaps the most serious need at the present time, especially from the point of view of immediate utility, is fuller information as to the composition and digestibility of British fodders. This need is most felt in the case of coarse fodders such as hay and straw whose composition and digestibility vary greatly according to variety, cultivation and harvesting. It is obviously most unsatisfactory that farmers should have to rely on German figures for information as to such materials. To provide the necessary information a routine survey of British fodders is required, and such a survey is in progress at Cambridge. A survey of the composition and feeding value of the mangold crop was completed some time ago. At the present time the various kinds of straws are under investigation. A preliminary leaflet has been issued and the final report will be ready shortly.

Turning to the more scientific side of the work, a point already referred to, the varying composition of the proteins of different foods, has received much attention. At present the results achieved have not gone beyond a revision of the methods of protein hydrolysis and separation of the hydrolytic products. Some years of scientific work will be necessary before the information gained is likely to be of practical importance. It is all the more necessary therefore to prosecute the work with all the resources which are available.

Another point of scientific interest is the observation that the skin temperatures of animals of the same breed kept under similar conditions show considerable variations, and that on the whole animals with a high skin temperature convert a smaller proportion of their food into meat than animals with a low skin temperature. A large calorimeter was in process of construction with a view to the pursuit of this line of investigation but, like many other things, its completion must wait for happier times.

Statistical investigations are in progress on the question of the relation between the amount of food consumed and the amount of meat produced.

Results already published indicate the possibility of important economies in meat production. So far the investigations have been confined to the process of fattening for beef and mutton. They are now being extended to growth, in the hope of throwing light on the cost of production of beef at different ages.

It appears to be generally recognized that in the future the country must make every possible endeavour to become more nearly self-supporting as regards food supply. The production of meat for human food is under any conditions a wasteful process. During 20 weeks of fattening a bullock eats something like 7 tons of turnips or mangolds, $\frac{3}{4}$ ton of hay or straw, and $\frac{1}{2}$ ton of cake or meal, in all about 2 tons of dry food, in order to increase in weight about $2\frac{1}{2}$ cwt. In other words about 16 lb. of dry food is required to produce 1 lb. of increased carcase weight. This statement at once suggests that there should be room for economy in beef production. The science of nutrition bears as directly on the keeping of horses and the production of bacon and milk as on the production of fat.

The live-stock industry involves enormous capital—Heape estimates it at over £400,000,000—and is responsible for over half the meat supply and nearly the whole milk supply of the nation.

It requires no special pleading to show the importance of the application of scientific method to an industry of this magnitude. The principles of nutrition of farm animals have been worked out on a basis which is as essentially scientific as that which underlies the practice of medicine or engineering. Work is in progress which will rapidly bring these principles into more direct practical touch with British conditions. The exigencies of the war have compelled even the most conservative of farmers to recognize how directly scientific knowledge can help them in buying and using the cheaper foods on the market. It remains for those of us who are responsible for the scientific side of the subject to extend our knowledge and our teaching, or we may lose the opportunity thus afforded of influencing stock-keepers in the direction of economy in production.

# GEOLOGY AS AN ECONOMIC SCIENCE

By Herbert H. Thomas, Sc.D.

*Secretary of the Geological Society of London.*

Geological science is the necessary outcome of the relations between Man as a reasoning being and the inanimate Earth on which he lives, and as such has gradually evolved from the dark ages of untutored observation and superstitious beliefs. There existed a Geology, and there were geologists such as Lehmann, Guettard and Werner, previous to the nineteenth century, but the true science had its birth a little more than a hundred years ago, as soon as it was recognised that the strata forming the Earth's crust were not thrown together in a fortuitous manner, but were superposed the one upon the other in a definite and invariable sequence. The work of William Smith in Britain, and of Cuvier, Brongniart and Lamarck in France, demonstrated, even to the most sceptical, that the various strata exposed at the surface could be traced, by means of definite characters that they possessed and by the fossil-organisms that they contained, over wide areas; and what was still more important, could be identified and relegated to their proper position in the sequence, even when met with in isolated masses and in widely separated districts.

Since the days of William Smith, and the foundation of the Geological Society of London in 1807, the rapid accumulation of fresh facts, their coordination and correct interpretation, have tended more and more to lift the science from regions of unwarranted speculation and to raise it to heights of exactitude little dreamt of by its founders; in fact "no more interesting record of human endeavour and achievement can be found than that presented by the advance of geology" during the last hundred years.

In some countries the strata are so nearly horizontal that one deposit occupies large areas; and thus no variety is met with except in those cases where some mountain-top permits of the preservation of a higher layer, or some deep valley is cut down into an underlying formation. Our country, although neither particularly mountainous nor deeply sculptured, stands alone in the great variety of rock-types it contains, and in presenting for study an almost unbroken series of geological formations—formations that by reason of their inclination follow each other across the country in rapid succession. It is this complexity of geological deposits, and at the same time com-

## THE SCOPE OF GEOLOGY

parative simplicity of geological structure, that points to Britain, above all other countries, as the ideal birthplace of geological science, especially of that part of geology which deals with the relative ages and normal superposition of the stratified deposits.

Geology, as a pure science, stands for all that pertains to the past history of our planet, and by a careful study of natural processes now in operation seeks to outline the train of events which has caused the Earth to assume its present external form and internal structure. Viewed from an economic standpoint, however, the chief aim of geology is accurately to define the distribution and relationships of the diverse mineral-masses or strata that form the accessible portion of the Earth's crust in which are stored so many substances intimately connected with our personal and national requirements.

The bearing of geology upon our economic life is probably not fully appreciated by those unacquainted with the science, but it is no exaggeration to state that there is hardly an industry or art that has not been, and is not, aided directly by the knowledge that geologists have accumulated, and that is not in some measure dependent on geological knowledge for its successful continuance.

Above all, the service that geology has rendered to the industries has been the spreading of sound and reasonable ideas regarding the nature and distribution of the useful minerals, the finding of solutions for those structural problems which arise in the course of their exploitation, and the aid it has given in the discovery of new sources of supply.

## Geological Maps.

Of all the instruments for the furtherance of our commercial welfare that geology has placed in the hands of an educated public, geological maps, undoubtedly, have exerted the most powerful and beneficial influence; and in the future they will be called upon to play a still more important part as the necessity arises for conserving, and at the same time deriving every possible advantage from, our remaining natural resources. So much of economic value depends upon a correct understanding of the superficial and underground distribution of the geological formations, that a geological map on which the outcrops of the various strata are traced, their inclination given, and the chief lines of disruption indicated, forms the most natural basis for all enquiries concerning the presence and exploitation of those useful materials obtained by mining or quarrying, for solving the complex problems connected with water-supply, and for dealing satisfactorily with questions relating to the distribution of vegetation.

The fact that such maps were capable of construction was first demonstrated by William Smith, Greenough, and MacCulloch, in the early decades of the nineteenth century. In 1834 Sir Henry De la Beche having pointed out the great benefits that were likely to accrue from a systematic survey of our Islands, a government survey was initiated; and there is no better commentary on this piece of departmental foresight than that the example of the United Kingdom was followed rapidly by our colonies, at their request, and by every other civilized nation.

The early workers in Britain laboured under difficulties imposed by the small scale and imperfections of the topographical maps, by the somewhat immature state of the science, and through the urgent necessity of completing a survey as rapidly as possible. These difficulties, however, did not prevent the surveyors from finishing a piece of work, the economic value of which was far in excess of the cost of production.

The surveyors' map, constructed on a scale of one inch to one mile—a scale eminently suited to pioneer-work—at once threw much light on the distribution of coal, metals, and other useful materials. In the case of coal, it laid down, for the first time, the limits of those strata in which and beneath which it is useless to search for coal, the outcrops of those formations which normally contain coal in this country, and the surface-position of those deposits under which beds of coal might reasonably lie concealed. The result of such a survey, therefore, was, amongst others, to give a clear idea as to the actual and possible limits of our coal-fields, and definite indications as to where further prospecting would be either useful or profitless. Unfortunately, even since detailed geological maps have been available for public reference, ignorance or lack of confidence has caused much capital to be expended in the abortive search for coal in places where the very nature of the geological formations forbids its presence.

The topographical re-survey of Great Britain, on a scale of six inches to one mile, has allowed of those beautiful maps of the Ordnance Survey being made the foundation on which to place the detailed geological work that was found by experience to be necessary for the correct understanding of the superficial and underground structure of mining or industrial areas.

There is, perhaps, a feeling amongst those less acquainted with geology and its applications that the construction of a geological map is a mechanical process, and that when once the surface has been surveyed and the information recorded nothing more remains to be done. This, however, is far from the truth, for in a country such as ours where vegetation and superficial accumulations occupy large areas, the natural exposures are not continuous but are hidden locally. It is one of the duties of the geological surveyor to note all these natural exposures, and from a study of them to lay down on his map a suggested continuation of the solid strata beneath the superficial deposits. It frequently happens that the available natural evidence renders possible more than one interpretation of the geological structure of a certain area, and it is then that shallow excavations such as railway-cuttings, tunnels, wells and drains, as well as all mining operations, aid the geologist in the correctness of his views. It will thus be seen that after a map has been constructed on the basis of natural exposures, there still remains the patient gathering of information from all those artificial excavations that may be made from time to time; such new data, by confirming or modifying the position of geological boundaries, enhancing the value of the map by virtue of increased accuracy.

It must be borne in mind that the possible utility of a geological map varies directly as the scientific character of its mode of construction; for unless the mapping is carried out by observers who are thoroughly acquainted with the principles of geology, and who are capable of calling to their aid those other sciences with which geology is so intimately bound up, the resulting maps will contain inconsistencies, misconceptions, and even fallacies. At the same time if scientific results are to be utilised fully by the community, it is a necessity that those to whom such results are to be of the most practical value should at least understand the principles of the science concerned.

*Coal.*

When we consider the economic history of the British Isles, we cannot fail to recognise that our great commercial prosperity in the past, more especially since the seventeenth century, has been due in no small measure to our mineral-wealth, more particularly to our vast stores of coal and iron. But in addition to these essentials, our Islands furnish us with large quantities of other useful metallic and non-metallic substances which have enabled us to build up and carry on a variety of industries.

Although geology as a science owes much to mining operations, it is a correct knowledge of geological principles that guides the miner in his costly undertakings, and it is ignorance or disregard of these principles that so often renders his efforts fruitless. Not only is a complete knowledge of the geological structure of a mining-district a necessary premise for the location of mineral-masses, but only by the utilisation of such knowledge can any deposit be exploited to the greatest advantage with the minimum of waste. In the past the working of a thick seam, a seam yielding the maximum amount of coal at a minimum cost, has often been carried on over large areas, as in Staffordshire and North Wales, with absolute disregard of valuable coal-seams that occur above and below. As the exhaustion of the thick coal proceeded, the mines were abandoned, so that now the cost of unwatering the old workings practically prohibits the exploitation of the lower seams, and should this task be undertaken it is carried on at considerable risk. Further, the caving in of the chambers in a thick seam has often reduced higher coals to an unworkable condition.

Geology now furnishes a means of determining not only the horizontal and vertical extent of mineral-deposits, but at the same time will act as a guide to the most profitable method of extraction. To this end every available piece of information with regard to our existing coal-fields is being collected and utilised by the Geological Survey.

It is with respect to concealed coal-fields, those coal-bearing rocks overlain, and therefore hidden, by newer formations, that geology has rendered, and will continue to render, such signal service to the nation. It is due to the careful labour of the geologist that extensions of our visible coal-fields have been proved to exist, and that new and entirely concealed fields have been discovered. The great extensions of the Yorkshire and Nottinghamshire coal-fields, as well as those of Northumberland, Durham, Lancashire, Somerset and Gloucestershire, are cases in point; while the discovery of the Kentish coal-field was also the direct result of scientific deduction.

It is interesting to note that according to the report of the Royal Commission in 1905, in a period of thirty years, geology has been the means of indicating coal-bearing areas that represent an addition of some 50,000 millions of tons to the available coal-supply of this country.

There remain large areas in Britain of which the extent and productiveness are still unproved, and it is these, as well as the detection of other concealed coal-fields, that will claim the attention of geologists in the future. The time that will elapse before the unproved be proved and the undiscovered detected depends entirely on how systematic an underground exploration by boring will be permitted, and on the condition that geologists are allowed a free hand in attacking the problems with which they are confronted.

## *Oil.*

For a great number of years the supply of petroleum was obtained from a few districts, and only from wells and deposits located by chance. As the demand increased and new supplies had to be sought for, a scientific study of proved fields was undertaken, with the result that the search was shown to be essentially a geological problem, and one in which geological structure was a controlling factor. The prospecting for mineral-oils, therefore, has been placed on a scientific basis and is being prosecuted by trained geologists, in all parts of the world where the geological formations and geological structure indicate success, in a manner which has

# METALLIFEROUS MINING

done much to remove, once and for all, the wasteful and uncertain methods on which we relied previously.

## *The Metals.*

Owing to the usual mode of occurrence of metalliferous minerals, their mining is fraught with increased difficulties. They occur as irregular masses in association with igneous rocks and in various ways which cause them to present a set of problems quite distinct from those of the stratified deposits. But the geologist by a thorough investigation of our own and foreign mineral-deposits has been able to establish a series of laws, and to formulate a number of working theories, that have had a profound influence on the methods of prospecting and on modern mining in general.

The structural difficulties encountered in metalliferous mining, such as the pinching-out of veins, their faulting, and other disturbances to which metalliferous deposits are prone, are those which can only be met and overcome by a knowledge of geological principles; but it is particularly in relation to the mode of occurrence of metalliferous deposits that geology has rendered the greatest service. With the introduction of precise petrological methods, geologists were equipped with another weapon with which to attack a number of problems of which there appeared to be no definite solution. By its use the geologist was enabled to detect delicate shades of lithological variation, and to give to the world, for the first time, some idea of the definite relationship that mineral-deposits bear to the country-rock in which they occur, and to throw new light on the genesis of the deposits as a whole.

The work that has been carried out, in recent years, on the petrology of ore-deposits and on the genesis of metalliferous veins marks a great advance; for the association of metalliferous minerals with certain rock-types, the increase or decrease in richness of mineral-deposits in depth, the secondary enrichment of the upper portions of lodes, and the tracing of alluvial deposits to their source, all present problems which the geologist has been called upon to solve. It is thus that the investigations into the mode of occurrence and origin of the iron-ores of Northern Europe, the lead-deposits of the United States, the zinc-ores of Greece, and the gold-deposits of Canada, South Africa and Victoria, are a few outstanding examples in which the results of geological studies of an academic character have proved of the greatest value to the practical miner.

*Water-supply.*

With the centralization of industry and the consequent segregation of population, the question of the supply of pure water in sufficient quantity is of ever-growing importance. Whether such a supply be obtained from superficial or underground sources, it is controlled by the geological structure of the district. Although any supply of water depends primarily on the rainfall in the catchment-area, it is the relative porosity of the strata, their retentive capacity, and the position of their outcrops that together determine the position of springs, and whether such springs shall be permanent or intermittent. In cases of supplies obtained from some underground porous strata, it is the geologist who informs the well-sinker as to the thickness of strata through which he will have to bore before water is obtained, and who by a careful delineation of geological boundaries knows whether the supply is likely to prove lasting. From his knowledge of the strata he would be able to state whether the water was likely to be fresh or salt, hard or soft, and in addition he would be in a position to advise what steps should be taken to preserve it from contamination.

It is obvious, therefore, that detailed mapping of the geological formations at the surface, and calculations as to their underground position and extent, are necessary for a proper understanding and conservation of our supply of pure water.

Fortunately, many of our large towns are situated on impervious strata that rest upon porous rocks of which the outcrop is situated beyond the region of possible contamination, such for instance as London and many towns in central and eastern England. The London Clay and other deposits overlying the

Chalk are now pierced by hundreds of wells which derive an almost unlimited supply of water from the lower porous deposit. Similarly in other parts of Britain we have such famous water-bearing strata as the sand-rocks of the Jurassic System, extending from the south to the north-east of England; and the lower portion of the New Red Sandstone which occupies the centre of England and passes northwards on either side of the Pennines. In other countries, such as in the arid regions of Australia and northern Africa, the application of geological knowledge has led to the utilisation of underground water-supplies which have done much to render these districts habitable and productive.

In any future scheme for the proper and uniform control of our national water-resources, the geological structure of all our river-basins and catchment-areas will have to be set out in great detail, and the underground contours of our porous water-bearing strata correctly given. As has been said already, geological maps of such a scale as six inches to one mile—the scale adopted by the Geological Survey—are the foundation of all questions concerning water-supply, whether it be superficial or underground. Superficial supplies are self-evident, but the proper understanding of an underground supply depends on calculations made by the geologist from surface-observations, checked from time to time by a careful record of borings or sinkings that may be made to the water-bearing strata.

## Civil-engineering.

In an address delivered before the Institution of Civil Engineers some few years ago we find it asserted that "few sciences are more intimately connected with civil engineering than geology" for, as the author points out, whether the work be the construction of railways, harbours, docks, canals, water-works or sewage-works, it necessitates the removal of large masses of rock, sand, clay or other geological material, with the lateral extent, thickness, and general characters of which the geologist is acquainted.

Thus one of the fundamental requirements of the engineer before such work is undertaken is a detailed geological survey of the district concerned. To take a case in point: in the construction of the great reservoir in the Vyrnwy Valley, from which to supply the city of Liverpool with water, geological principles guided the engineer in the choice of the position for the dam; a position so advantageously selected that any other site, even as little as 200 yards away, would have involved an additional expenditure of from £300,000 to £400,000.

In the construction of a railway, the making of cuttings and tunnelling through the hills, the inclination and hardness of the rocks, the presence of water-bearing strata, and the occurrence of faults, are a few of the geological factors with which the engineer must acquaint himself before his work is commenced, unless he is willing to run the risk of unnecessary labour and expenditure. We have only to turn to the accounts of such undertakings as the laying out of the Great Western Railway by Brunel, the cutting of the Suez Canal by De Lesseps, the piercing of the Alps, the projected Channel Tunnel, and the complicated system of tube-railways beneath the metropolis, to see how dependent these schemes are for their success on the information that geology is in a position to supply.

*Agriculture.*

The modern science of Ecology, if demonstration were needed, has clearly shown how close is the connexion between geology and agriculture. It is obvious that the character and composition of the soil and subsoil of any particular area are dependent upon the weathering and disintegration of solid rocks, and on various geological processes that have operated within the district. There is no doubt that large-scale geological maps showing the disposition of the superficial accumulations are of considerable use to the agriculturist, for, as constructed by the Geological Survey, they clearly distinguish between soils due to disintegration and those due to transport.

Questions as to the suitability of certain soils for certain purposes, as to matters of drainage and the use of artificial and natural manures, will all be answered more satisfactorily if a knowledge of geological principles be allowed to influence the considerations.

### *The record of facts for future use.*

In the early days of the science Sir Charles Lyell urged geologists to multiply and record observations and patiently await the result at some future period. He pointed out in the clearest manner possible how geological knowledge gained from one suite of observations makes the next step more easy, and lends precision where doubt had previously existed. Looking back over the last century we recognise how, again and again, seemingly disconnected facts have banded themselves together to give rise to some geological principle of far-reaching economic importance.

With all that geology has accomplished, the further accumulation of geological facts and the recording of observations, have not diminished in importance; for only by the advance of knowledge is it possible to raise the standard of general education and, indirectly, of industrial efficiency. Fortunately the surface of the land changes its form so slowly that, in most cases, geological observations can be made with ease and verified at leisure. Such observations are being made by a multitude of skilled geologists and recorded for future reference in the pages of various scientific publications; also, the Geological Survey, in the process of making its detailed maps, besides gathering material for immediate use, of necessity collects a vast amount of information which has economic value of a potential kind.

What has been said refers more particularly to surface-observations, but in our mining-districts underground work permits of facts being collected which have an obvious and highly important bearing on the economy of, at least, the area concerned, if they are not of wider application.

In the majority of cases colliery-owners, water-engineers and others who realise the debt they owe to geological science gladly permit geologists to record and make use of the scientific results of their excavations, but with the inadequate machinery that exists at present for the collection of such details, much valuable information is inevitably lost.

The geological knowledge of our country has now reached such a state of efficiency that further advance with regard to the understanding of the structure of our coal-fields, and more particularly of their extensions, is largely dependent on exploration by boring and the examination of the rock-cores so obtained. In this connexion it is a striking anomaly that any individual is permitted to open quarries and make excavations, to sink shafts and make bore-holes, and to undertake work of similar character, without placing on record any of the scientific results that may be obtained, or even specifying the locality at which his operations were carried on. In certain cases commercial competition renders it advisable that information so obtained should be temporarily withheld, but this is surely no excuse for the indefinite retention and ultimate loss of knowledge which after a time ceases to be of value to the owner but is of infinite value to the State. Take for example the case of a bore-hole made in search for coal or other minerals. If it proves to the owner of the property that no mineral-wealth, such as he sought, exists, that information can be of no value to him, but this fact if placed on record will prevent, in the future, wasteful expenditure of capital in the same area to obtain the same negative result. Such remarks apply equally to the question of water-supply, for the same careful record of scientific information concerning its underground distribution is an absolute necessity for our well-being.

Such considerations as these naturally suggest certain lines of action, and the most obvious is for legislation to demand that all excavations, bore-holes, and shafts, that reach a depth of more than 50 feet from the surface, should be notified to some government department whose duty it should be to register the details, and place on record those facts of scientific value which the work has brought to light. That there are difficulties in the way of carrying out such a scheme must be admitted. In the first place, the strata exposed in any excavation or bore-hole must be studied by those whose knowledge of geological principles enables them alone correctly to interpret the facts laid bare and to render them of the greatest value for future reference. Again, as the work is of a temporary character the government department concerned should have the right of inspection during the time that the work is in progress. But the chief difficulty at the moment is that the Geological Survey, a part of whose duties consists in the collection and registration of such details, could not undertake the task of systematically examining and recording all bore-holes without a considerably augmented staff.

The chief complaint likely to be made by the individual would be, in his opinion, the premature publication of details which he had collected at his own expense for his own benefit; but his objections would probably be met by regarding such information as he might supply as confidential for a statutory period, or for a shorter period during which he might be interested in the commercial undertaking of which the bore-hole or excavation formed a part. Whatever objections may be raised and difficulties met with, it is quite certain that in the future we cannot afford to disregard and leave to chance the collection of the valuable geological information furnished by bore-holes and similar undertakings, and there is no question that steps should be taken for the systematic preservation of such records of national importance.

That there should be a national exploration of our remaining mineral-resources is the firm conviction of many. With regard to this question, as well as with respect to that of the registration of bore-holes and other excavations, we cannot do better than quote a past president of the Geological Society who said that "Unless something of this sort is done, and done in a systematic and masterful manner, we run a great risk of frittering away the most important of our national resources left to us, of destroying confidence, of wasting time and money at a most precious and critical period of our history, and of slipping down hill at a time when our equipment and resources are ready to enable us to stride forward." If these remarks were a fair statement of the case in times of peace, how much more forceful they appear to-day.

### *The effect of the War.*

One of the results of the great struggle in which we are engaged has been to produce a keener appreciation of the debt that the Country owes to the prosecution of pure science, to work undertaken in most cases with no thought of reward other than the feeling of satisfaction which arises from the knowledge that an advance has been made, and that the world may benefit thereby. In the case of geology, perhaps more than most of the other natural sciences, the general public has failed to grasp how intimately it is connected with the welfare of our kingdom and its dependencies.

The limitation of our imports of raw and manufactured material from foreign countries, and the call for an increased output of many commodities, have caused us to take a census of our own resources, to manufacture articles previously imported from abroad, and to modify our manufacturing processes in such a manner as to render us less dependent on foreign raw-material—material often introduced into this country to the neglect or detriment of our home or colonial supplies.

The use of imported material has, in some cases, been the result of the more systematic working of the foreign deposits and the utilisation of the by-products; in other cases it has legitimately arisen because the foreign raw-material is either more abundant or of better quality than our own, but the importation of raw-material from abroad is often controlled by fashion, and not by the fact that there is no similar and equally suitable material at home; and as an instance of this we may cite the extensive use of foreign sands, clays, and road-metal, all articles which with equal facility could be obtained from our own country. This blind following of a fashion is the direct result of a lack of scientific knowledge, coupled with the incapacity to appreciate those scientific reasons which render certain materials suitable for a special purpose. Now, however, there is arising a better under-

# THE POSITION OF PURE SCIENCE

standing and a feeling of mutual dependence between science and industrial enterprise. The great mass of scientific information that the geological surveys, and geologists in general, have collected and made available in maps and other publications, is being drawn upon more fully; the geological teaching of our universities and technical institutions is making itself felt in a manner unequalled in the past; and new lines of research are being initiated as the result of our altered conditions.

We can only hope that in the future pure science will have a foremost place in the sympathies of those who direct and control our national affairs, so that by its encouragement we can eliminate from our national life the wasteful principle of trial and error and substitute sound reasoning for the empiricism of the past.

# MEDICINE AND EXPERIMENTAL SCIENCE

By F. Gowland Hopkins, F.R.S.

*Professor of Biochemistry in the University of Cambridge.*

During the early days of the war of 1870 the surgeon Sédillot wrote as follows to the President of the French Academy, "The horrible mortality amongst the wounded in battle calls for the attention of all the friends of science and humanity. The surgeon's art, hesitating and disconcerted, pursues a doctrine whose rules seem to flee before research....Places where there are wounded are recognisable by the fetor of suppuration and gangrene." Quoting this letter another French writer adds that, as a matter of fact, "Hundreds and thousands of wounded, their faces pale, but full of hope and desire to live, succumbed between the eighth and tenth day to gangrene and erysipelas. Those failures of surgery of the past are plain to us now that the doctrine of germs has explained everything; but at that time such an avowal of impotence before the mysterious *contagium sui generis* which the doctors averred eluded all research, and such awful statistics of mortality, embittered the anguish of defeat." Yet this was in Pasteur's own land, the home of researches which ten years earlier had already given the clearest indications as to how such tragedies might be avoided or mitigated. Humanity in the mass is slow to see the significance of new knowledge, and the professors of the art of surgery were in those days averse from adopting new methods, especially when, as in this case, the suggestions came from a source apparently unconnected with their art.

In this country, however, there was one man at least, who, endowed with the practical genius of his race, but possessed also of the instinct and experience of an investigator, had appraised, appreciated, and utilised the teaching of Pasteur. For three years or more before the war Lister had begun to fight sepsis with antiseptics, and months before the wounded from the fields of Wörth and Gravelotte lay rotting in the hospitals of France he had shown to all men how thousands of them might have been saved. Yet it occurred to no one in France—during the first battles at any rate —to make any use of the new methods. If from the tragedies of the present war the horror of sepsis has been largely absent, it is to the work of Pasteur and the experimentalists who have followed in his footsteps that the chief credit must be given. Organisation and increase in professional skill have played their part in the betterment, but they would have been of small account without the knowledge and direction supplied by the labour of scientific research.

If this be true of wound sepsis it is equally true respecting the absence of typhoid fever from the sodden trenches of the western front. Prophylaxis and organisation have kept this scourge at bay, but scientific knowledge alone has supplied the methods of prophylaxis and directed the organisation. Now, the British nation is quick to appreciate and applaud a practical outcome such as this; but it has less appreciation for, and unfortunately little knowledge of, the labours which have made the outcome possible. Our people as a whole respect the practical physician and are grateful for his ministrations, but they are vague as to the source of his knowledge.

The practice of Medicine is, in its essence, an Art. It is an art which calls for high personal qualifications, because it has to be applied amid the intricacies of human nature, and must ever take account of the prejudices, the sensibilities, the hopes, fears and reserves of complex human beings. More than any other art, however, does it call for abundant scientific knowledge. For centuries Medicine was based wholly upon tradition. It was then unprogressive. For a few generations, having shaken off the trammels of tradition and authority, it was an art based upon the results of observation. It then progressed; but slowly.

For a couple of generations its practice has been based upon the results of experiment as well as upon observation, and its progress has been rapid. It will be found that most laymen in this country who have not given thought to the matter vaguely assume that the progress of medical knowledge still depends solely or mainly upon the accumulation of experience gained at the bedside. The truth that untiring labour in scores of scientific laboratories has been the chief factor in the rapid progress of recent years has not yet come home to the public. Experience at the bedside and the habit of close observation are indeed essential for the making of a successful physician. These and these alone can qualify him for the successful application of knowledge to the relief of human suffering; but history shows that the knowledge itself grew very slowly when bedside observations were its chief source.

In a short article no proper survey of the history of medicine can be attempted, but it is desirable that an attempt should be made to give some indication of its position, and of the kind of progress it was making, in the middle period of the last century. It was then that experimental science began for the first time to exert an appreciable influence upon it. During the seventeenth century the classical tradition which had been so fatal to progress was very nearly slain; our countryman, Harvey, giving it one of its most fatal wounds.

The characteristic scepticism of the eighteenth century had a healthy influence upon medical practice, the absurd medication of the middle ages being gradually, though slowly and grudgingly, given up. Another tendency of this century, however, its delight in speculation and deduction, stood in the way of medical advance. "What a vast literature," writes Sir William Osler, referring to our knowledge of fevers, "exists between Sydenham and Broussais. What a desolate sea of theory and speculation!" This desolation extended from the middle of the seventeenth to the early years of the nineteenth century. On the nearer shore of the sea, where speculation gave way to the solid ground of observations properly recorded, we see the heroic figure of the Frenchman Louis (born 1787). "For nearly seven years, including the flower of his bodily and mental powers (from the age of 33 to 40) he consecrated the whole of his time and talents to rigorous impartial observation. All private practice was relinquished and he allowed no consideration of personal emoluments to interfere with the resolution he had formed. For some time his extreme minuteness of inquiry and accuracy of description was the subject of sneering and ridicule, and 'To what end?' was not unfrequently and tauntingly asked...." Nevertheless it was in no small part due to Louis' influence that half way through the last century clinical teaching and clinical practice had become essentially

# THE METHOD OF OBSERVATION 233

sound. Enlightened practitioners were saying: "Let us cease to pour drugs of which we know little into bodies of which we know less"; indiscriminate blood letting was being given up, and the leaders of the profession were not only admirable bedside observers, but were awake to the importance of records made, in accordance with the teaching of Louis, on a numerical basis. Moreover the custom of checking the results of clinical observation by means of *post mortem* examinations was beginning to add greatly to empirical knowledge, and to the accuracy of diagnosis.

At this middle point of the nineteenth century our own country was fortunate in possessing for its medical leaders men of great intellectual power and attainments. Let us note how one of them writes concerning his own methods. William Jenner, following in the footsteps of Louis, had been striving to make it clear to his English colleagues that Typhus and Typhoid Fever are distinct pathological entities. His views, though of course sound and correct, met with opposition and criticism. "I considered, therefore," he writes in the preface to his book on fevers published in 1850, "that it was necessary to begin *de novo*, and consult only the voice of nature—convinced that, although the most intellectual might fail at first to comprehend her often ambiguous language, yet that her most humble votaries might by patience and daily watching, by keeping honest record of every sound she uttered—by joining letter to letter, adding word to word, and line to line—at last spell out her meaning and so reach that rank which the great master of induction tells us man may legitimately hope to attain, namely, that of her interpreter." Here in fine terms we have an epitome of what the method of the Observer should be. If progress with such ideals is not rapid it must be due to limitations in the method.

The high ideal expressed in the words of Jenner just quoted was attained by many of his leading contemporaries, and medicine certainly made progress in their hands. If we consider closely, however, what was being done, we find it was chiefly on the negative lines of getting rid of unsound dogma. Careful clinical work, checked by morphological anatomy, was removing the fanciful from medical views and practice. New and significant knowledge came; but it came very slowly.

In a country rich in gold observant wayfarers may find nuggets on their path, but only systematic mining can provide the currency of nations. In the search for natural knowledge the Experimentalists are the miners. Jenner felt the ambiguity of nature's chance remarks, but saw apparently no remedy save in the laborious recording of her spontaneous utterings and a painful effort at interpretation. Nature, however, can be taken into the witness box and directly questioned; moreover the questions can be so put that there

# THE METHOD OF EXPERIMENT 235

is no possibility of ambiguity in the answer. This is the method of experiment. It was the method of Pasteur.

Consider further for a moment the growth of our knowledge concerning acute fevers during the period which just preceded the work of Pasteur. Jenner's observations, and the clear inductive reasoning he based upon them, left the medical world convinced that typhoid and typhus fevers were distinct diseases. The bedside studies of such men as Louis, Bartlett, Murchison, and many others made for sound views and for a healthy recognition of ignorance. Descriptions became more accurate; the significance of this or that symptom became better evaluated as the result of statistical records, and a sharper classification became possible. Nothing was added, however, that appreciably widened the point of view; nothing that could remove the utter vagueness concerning the essential nature and cause of fevers, or throw light on the mysteries of contagion. In this respect the knowledge of the middle of the nineteenth century scarcely differed from that of the days of Sydenham. To a new era belonged that moment when Pasteur, intruding into a vague discussion concerning the 'cause' of puerperal fever, rushed to the blackboard, made a rapid sketch of a microbe and cried "Tenez, voici sa figure!" It is a great thing to see the face of the enemy.

The microbic origin of disease is a fact of nature which might well have for ever eluded the methods of clinical observation and morbid anatomy. It could not possibly elude the methods of Pasteur.

Pasteur's first researches dealt with a region of fact which seemed remote enough from the interests of practical medicine, though a region of great importance to science. It was already known to chemists that certain substances exist in two distinct, though closely related, forms, identical in all their properties save that the one form in transmitting polarised light twists the ray to the right, while the other form twists it to the left. As a crystallographer Pasteur discovered that in such cases the crystals of the one form differ from those of the other with that kind of difference which is illustrated by the two hands of a man—essentially identical but not superimposable—one of them corresponding to the mirror image of the other. Sometimes a substance capable of existing in two such forms may, when in solution, show no action upon a ray of light. In such a case we now speak of the substance as being in the racemic form. In reality, as Pasteur showed, both active forms are then present, and these neutralise each other. We are now to see how a crystallographer, knowing little or nothing of medicine, came to inaugurate one of the greatest advances in our knowledge of disease.

It was, after all, a chance observation which constituted the first step! It was an observation, too, which to most minds, even scientific minds, might at that time have seemed trivial; but to Pasteur it seemed—as indeed it was—of profound significance. The Cambridge Medical School has done well to inscribe upon its new buildings a saying due to Pasteur himself, "*Dans les champs de l'observation le hasard ne favorise que les esprits préparés.*"

When a solution of a salt of tartaric acid in the form spoken of above as racemic had stood in his laboratory long enough to go 'mouldy,' or to undergo fermentation, Pasteur found that, of the two forms of tartrate present, one, and only one, had disappeared. We have seen that the two forms differ as little as does the right hand from the left, and yet the growth of the mould, or the action of the ferment, destroyed the one and left the other untouched. Why? The question greatly stirred the mind of Pasteur. Materials for its answer are woven in the very fabric of life itself. No discussion of it must be attempted here. We have only to note that the circumstance was sufficient to fix the attention of the great chemist and crystallographer, once and for all, upon the subject of fermentation. Further happy chance gave him, at the very time these observations were made, work and duties at Lille, the centre of a district where fermentations were a prominent local industry. Pasteur's passion for knowledge was only approached in intensity by his desire to make that knowledge useful to his country, and his surroundings at Lille stimulated the already keen desire to explore the whole subject of fermentation experimentally. He set himself to such experiments with great energy, the use of the microscope going hand in hand with chemical studies. He investigated among other cases the lactic acid fermentation which brings about the souring of milk, the butyric fermentation, and, in particular, alcoholic fermentation. To enlarge upon the importance of these, his earlier studies, would require pages; a bald statement calls for some imagination to illumine it. Briefly stated, what Pasteur established at this time was as follows: (1) The deepseated chemical changes which occur in fermentations of the kind studied are due to the presence and influence of living organisms, and not, as was believed and taught at the time, to the supposed circumstance that putrefying animal or vegetable matter transmits, in some very mysterious way, its state of active decomposition to other substances. (2) There is a special kind of organism the activities of which are correlated with each kind of fermentation. (3) Such organisms (bacteria, yeasts, etc.), are not born spontaneously in the decomposing or fermenting material, but are derived from 'infection.' They are born of parents like unto themselves, and multiply when they find themselves under favourable conditions. The last point, established by very beautiful and ingenious experimentation, in the teeth of opposed opinion, is by no means the least important. Upon the facts that these unicellular organisms arise from cells similar to themselves and, with certain minor qualifications, may be said always to breed true, are based the modern science of bacteriology, and the definiteness of our present knowledge concerning zymotic diseases. Even when at the early stage just described Pasteur's results were sufficient to convey to a receptive and logical mind like that of Lister an assurance of their future importance to medicine and surgery; but much had yet to be done to convince the sceptical. Pasteur himself, though not trained in medicine, contributed much in his later work towards establishing the importance of micro-organisms in disease. The advance made by others in bacteriological technique was, during his lifetime, so great as to leave him almost an amateur among experts in the narrow domain of pure technicalities; but there are few aspects of modern bacteriology which he did not foresee and initiate by pioneer experiments. From studies of wine and beer, which greatly helped French industries, he proceeded to the investigation of an infective silkworm disease, with results of considerable economic importance. He then investigated certain diseases of farm animals and earned the gratitude of the farmers. Finally he proceeded to the study of anthrax and rabies to the still more direct benefit of humanity. All this time the theoretical bearing of his experiments was greatly enriching science and medicine.

When at last he was in possession of his great Institute in Paris he was surrounded by medical men of all countries and for a time personally inspired their labours. Vallery-Radot, his biographer, uses words concerning Pasteur which may well close our reference to his work. "He felt that nothing could arrest the course of his doctrine, of which he said 'the breath of Truth is carrying it towards the fruitful fields of the future.' He had that intuition which makes a great poet of a great scientist. The innumerable ideas surging through his mind were like so many bees all trying to issue from the hive at the same time. So many plans and preconceived ideas only stimulated him to further researches; but when he was once started on a road he distrusted each step, and only progressed in the train of precise, clear, and irrefutable experiments."

"Precise, clear, and irrefutable experiments"; such were the starting point of modern bacteriology, and by the continuation of such experiments carried out in laboratories all over the world it has progressed. It now forms a remarkable body of knowledge, and as a formal science it is possessed of a highly developed and ingenious experimental technique. Its chief need, perhaps, in order to

# TANGIBLE CAUSES OF DISEASE

make its next great advance, is the assistance of a great chemist, such as he who presided at its birth.

Robert Koch to whom bacteriology owes many of its successful experimental methods formulated certain postulates which must be fulfilled before a particular organism can be held to be responsible for a given disease. It must be identified in the diseased tissues, cultivated outside the body, reproduce the same disease in animals, and again be found multiplying in the tissues of these animals. In connection with the great majority of infective and contagious diseases these criteria are now fulfilled, and we know the specific agent in each case. Consider how much this means. Before Pasteur, the physician, when face to face with a case of fever, had to act in complete ignorance of any tangible reason for the symptoms he beheld. If he thought about causation at all, little more than words and phrases were available for the assistance of his thought. Now he can actually handle the 'cause' of each fever. It is a living thing, having qualities and habits with which he can become intimate. As a consequence the whole attitude of the doctor's mind is altered. Diagnosis may be a matter of certainty; treatment has entered upon an entirely new era.

Since Pasteur, we have gradually come to recognise how great a part the lowest and most minute of living organisms play in the economy of nature, sometimes maleficent, often beneficial. At first our attention was turned wholly to vegetable cells and chiefly to bacteria. We had to wait longer before learning that minute organisms belonging rather to the animal kingdom are scarcely less intrusive in the scheme of things, and that a whole group of diseases is due to parasitic protozoa. The story of the development of our knowledge concerning such diseases is even more fascinating than the history of bacteriology, and tells of another triumph for the method of experiment.

Think of the ague fit, the objective symptom of malaria. Known to ancient Greece, painfully familiar to Rome; familiar throughout Europe in the middle ages; familiar indeed in our own country before its fens and marshes were drained. In illustration of its familiarity in England we may recall the account of Falstaff's symptoms given by the Hostess in Shakespeare's Henry V, "Ah! poor heart. He is so shaked of a burning quotidian tertian that it is most lamentable to behold." Here clearly was a point for the gallery, and Shakespeare must have felt sure of the gallery's acquaintance even with the medical terms used (or misused) concerning ague. To Britons as empire builders tropical malaria has always been a menace and a hindrance. For centuries it has been under the eye of the physician; even classical authors, from Hippocrates to Celsus, displaying remarkable knowledge of its clinical features. Millions have suffered from it throughout the ages, with their sufferings mitigated, it is true, for the last three centuries by the possession of quinine, one of the greatest discoveries of empiricism. A few years of experiment, however, and we learned enough of the natural history of this disease to be able to say that if administrative action were prompt and comprehensive enough no man need suffer from it again.

For some years after Laveran had described the parasite of malaria in the blood of patients it seemed as if little use could be made of the discovery, because the disease could not be communicated to animals, and so experiment seemed impossible. Then at last came the thought of Manson, the work of Ross, and the discovery that the mosquito is the 'intermediate host' of the parasite and the means of its transmission. The life-cycle of the latter was then worked out, and the whole subject of malaria so fully clarified that a control of the scourge has become a matter for organisation and administration alone. Later studies have added instance after instance of a disease having more or less similar relations. Knowledge of pathogenic protozoa, of the existence and nature of intermediate hosts, of transmission by bites of vermin, and of other significant facts, has robbed another group of diseases of its terror and is making the tropics habitable for all men. Our country may well be proud of its share in this great advance. It forms a triumph of science which should receive more attention in this article; but it is necessary to pass on.

In quite other directions the advance of experimental science has revolutionised medicine. Not all disease is due to parasitism. It may be due to disorders originating from some failure within the body itself. Until well within the middle of the last century studies of the human body had been largely anatomical and statical; resulting in accurate description but in little knowledge of dynamic functions. At the time, however, when Pasteur was beginning his studies physiologists were actively at work, and the functions of the body were being investigated at many centres. In Germany the school of Carl Ludwig was obtaining results of importance and, in France, Pasteur's contemporary and friend, Claude Bernard, was inspiring all the physiologists of Europe. Since then the centre of research has gradually shifted to this country, and we now possess physiologists who lead the world.

From the nature of things the results of experimental studies are usually somewhat in advance of their practical application, but physiology, pathology, and practical medicine are never very far removed from each other, a fact which may be illustrated—choosing one instance out of the many available—by brief reference to our recently won knowledge concerning internal secretions. The active glands of the body are functionally

# SECRETIONS

of two kinds; some provide secretions which enter the alimentary canal and secure the digestion of the food; others elaborate materials which pass into the blood and exercise an important influence in maintaining that nicely adjusted equilibrium in the living tissues which constitutes health. Neither observation of the intact body during life nor anatomical studies after death could possibly have thrown any light whatever upon the functions of the second class. The pancreas is a gland possessing both of the types of function mentioned. Its 'external' secretion is concerned with digestion, its 'internal' secretion with chemical equilibrium in the tissues. In connection with the former an extraordinary instance of correlation among the activities of different organs in the body was brought to light, fourteen years ago, by Bayliss and Starling. The proper progress of digestion requires that the external secretion of the pancreas should be poured upon the food as soon as the latter leaves the stomach for the intestines. How is this sequence of events secured in nature? The stomach provides an acid secretion for carrying out the preliminary stages of digestion, and when its contents pass into the intestine they are under normal circumstances strongly acid. Now the minute cells which line the surface of the intestine are in a peculiar way sensitive to the influence of acids. On contact with them they are immediately provoked to an act of internal secretion, and pour into the blood a substance which has been called 'secretin.' A supply of this substance in the blood is immediately secured therefore when the acid contents of the stomach enter the intestine. But by secretin the pancreas is affected as by no other substance, and when the blood which leaves the intestinal wall charged with secretin passes through the pancreas the gland is immediately stimulated to pour, by way of its duct, its special digestive fluid into the cavity of the intestine, where the partially digested food from the stomach awaits its action. Thus, automatically, are the physiological events adjusted in due sequence.

Turning now to the internal secretion of the pancreas, a product of quite another character, we have learnt from abundant experiments that its presence is absolutely necessary to all the living tissues of the body. In its absence the sugar which normally provides energy for their activities escapes utilisation, and the whole animal becomes diabetic. One organ caters for the needs of every other organ in the body.

Who, having visited the valleys of the Alps, is unfamiliar with the painful aspect of the cretin? The cretin's condition is due to failure in infancy of the internal secretion of the thyroid gland. Without a proper supply of this, the young body fails to grow into the normal semblance of mankind. If the same gland first loses its activity in later life the condition of Myxoedema results. The

# THE THYROID GLAND

individual becomes bloated, apathetic, and feeble in intellect. If, instead of failing, the activity of the thyroid becomes exaggerated at any time, another pathological condition supervenes; that of Exophthalmic Goitre or Graves' disease. In this is found over excitability of the nervous system, a tumultuous pulse, irritability, and, in general, over stimulation of tissue activity. The thyroid gland weighs but an ounce or so, but its functions are of extreme importance to the body. Certainly not less important are those of the suprarenal glands; small organs, one perched on each kidney, and weighing together no more than one fourth of an ounce. To describe in detail all the influence they exert upon the body would require the whole space allotted to this article. The best impression of the remarkable functions exerted by their internal secretion may be given by pointing out that many of the physiological events which accompany a strong emotion such as that of anger, and therefore many of the feelings associated with the emotion, arise from the circumstance that the primary psychological element of the emotion leads to nerve impulses which cause an increased secretion from these glands. Looking at the facts from a somewhat different angle we may say that upon the secretion of these small organs depend the physiological adjustments which make for safety upon emergency. The sight of an enemy or any realisation of danger increases the flow of the secretion, and the effect of this upon the body as a whole is to make it better prepared to meet the emergency. For fight or for flight; for any sort of strenuous action, the body needs those immediate adjustments which are produced by an increased flow from the suprarenal glands. This flow is brought about by the nervous disturbances which follow upon a realisation of emergency. Our knowledge of the remarkable relations of these glands has been gradually built up, mainly from the brilliant experimental researches of Schaefer, Langley, and Elliott, as well as others in this country, and from those of Cannon in America. It is one of the triumphs of the chemical side of physiology that the actual chemical substance present in the secretion and responsible for its remarkable effects has been isolated from the glands. Its constitution has been fully determined, and its artificial manufacture accomplished. It is known as Adrenalin. We could now stop any metaphysical discussion concerning the 'cause' of certain at least of the physiological events which accompany emotions by writing the chemical formula of adrenalin upon the blackboard and saying with Pasteur "*Tenez, voici sa figure!*" Facts no less interesting are associated with the internal secretion of the reproductive glands. These, in addition to executing their more obvious functions, pour into the blood substances of the profoundest importance to the normal development of the body and to some of its functions.

It is impossible to stop and appraise the effect upon medical thought and practice of the kind of knowledge which has been illustrated by these brief and very inadequate references. It is enough to point out at how great a relative disadvantage was the doctor when he had to minister to the body in ignorance of such things. Yet he was well nigh wholly ignorant of them a few years ago. Our present detailed knowledge of the central nervous system; of the localisation of function on the surface of the brain; of the significance of certain types of nerve cells and their processes; of the intricate course of the nerve tracts which carry this or that particular impulse, and such understanding as we may have of the nerve impulse itself, have arisen largely from experimental research. Although observations, made upon man, of the symptoms which follow upon injuries and disease occurring in known localities of the nervous system (observations which during a great war are only too frequent) have taught us much in this direction, it is only by abundant animal experiments that such knowledge can be systematised and consolidated.

Physiology is beginning to explain the true inwardness of diseases of metabolism—of gout, diabetes, and the like; and, by experiment, is learning much for the future service of medicine about the chemistry of living tissues generally. On these lines the more esoteric aspects of human nutrition are coming to light, and with knowledge of these we gain insight into the meaning of efficiency, and understand better how to secure the future health of infants and growing children. The new science of experimental pathology, in so far as it is not bacteriology, is based on the application of the methods of physiology to the study of diseased states. It is replacing the purely anatomical studies of the older pathologists and is welding physiology and practical medicine together. Experimental Psychology, again, is a growing science, with real accomplishment behind it, and of profound importance to our understanding of mental disease.

The influence of experimental research upon our power of treating disease forms the subject of a special article, but a few words may be added here. We have already seen that the medication of the middle ages, the heritage of a belief in magic, died very hard. Though empiricism could boast of isolated successes—such as that already mentioned, the discovery and use of quinine—there was little of rationality in the use of drugs until quite late in the history of medicine. The leading and more enlightened physicians of the last century, in reaction from the irrational, used but few drugs and used them sparingly. Then, as a branch from general physiology, arose the new science of pharmacology, which quantitatively estimates the exact effect of each drug upon every organ of the body. It early brought to light the 'selective' nature of drug action, and with the recognition of this began the rationalisation of therapeutics. A substance which exerts an influence in the body shows nearly always a greater affinity for one tissue and lesser affinity for others. Its action is selective. Clearly this gives the first indication for its rational use as a drug. The exact nature of its local action must next be determined, and then its minor and accessory effects. The extraordinary synthetic powers of modern organic chemistry enable us to obtain new compounds with selective actions on the body; and by gradually modifying in detail the general construction of a substance of known action we can intensify or modify that action as we will.

We cannot here follow up all that these efforts have meant to practical medication, but we can indicate what is their logical goal. In the case, for instance, of a disease due to a parasite we may hope to find or to make a drug which is so selective as between one living tissue and the others as to be poisonous and absolutely fatal to the parasite, and yet wholly harmless to the host. This would be a *specificum absolutum*, and its use would illustrate what we mean by wholly rational therapeutics. The ideal is not yet reached, but it has been approached in the employment of such drugs as salvarsan. In another direction treatment has attained to a wholly rational basis. When, as the result of disease, the body lacks a product made normally by itself the missing product may be directly supplied. The administration of sheep's thyroid gland to the cretin, first practised by Dr Murray of Newcastle, is an instance of treatment, magical in its results, but utterly rational in respect of its basis.

The third great line of advance towards rational treatment has followed the teaching yielded by the experimental study of natural immunity. Parasites such as bacteria kill, not by their mere presence in the body, but because they produce poisons. Now the body itself nearly always reacts to the poison of the parasite so as to produce a substance capable of either neutralising the poison or killing the poison producers. The human body may fail, however, to produce such substances with sufficient rapidity, and it then succumbs to the attack of the enemy. What could be more rational than to assist it by giving the very same protective substances obtained from animals which have been so treated as to produce them in excess? This is the modern serum treatment, which, together with treatment by vaccines, a method based upon allied but somewhat different principles, has already secured great triumphs. It is a very new thing, however, and when developed will show triumphs greater still. In therapeutics, then, the experimental method is gradually replacing the irrational by the rational.

Such illustrations as have already been given will perhaps suffice for the purpose of this article and show how great is the debt of clinical medicine to experimental science. The art of the physician remains, as before, a noble and difficult one, which must always call for special personal endowments; but experiment has widened the knowledge on which it is based, and experiment alone could have secured the progress which the last half century has witnessed.

A matter which is of moment to any serious reader must be touched on before closing. While scientific advances of every kind tend to react upon and assist medicine it is certain that without experiments upon animals the subject cannot properly advance. The necessity continually arises for performing preliminary experiments upon living animals before this or that new piece of knowledge can be applied to the relief of humanity. Much of the new knowledge can, indeed, only be won by means of such experiments. The alternatives are three: ignorance and lack of progress; experiments upon human beings; or experiments upon animals. It should not be difficult to choose among them. The emotions which have led many to reject the last alternative are among those deserving the highest respect. Such emotions, however, have too often been allowed to express themselves in combination with ignorance and with an absence of all sense of proportion. If after the war the nation awakes to a sense of its responsibility in connection with advancement of knowledge every man and woman will take care to make himself or herself fully informed upon this subject. The experimentalist has nothing to fear, but everything to gain, from the formation of an informed and healthy public opinion concerning his work  It is what he most hopes for.

There remains an infinite amount to be done before all that is still obscure about disease and its treatment can be made clear. This is plain to us from our present standpoint, and fresh knowledge will reveal, as it always does, unsuspected ignorance. It is to be hoped that this country, during the period of reconstruction after the war, will recognise that medical science is itself a reconstructive force. It must heal, so far as possible, those whom the war has broken, and so help to provide workers for the immediate future. It must watch the public health during the strain of exceptional effort which is to come. It must teach the nation how best to rear the generation which is next to bear the burden. Our people should take more interest in its advance.

It was characteristic of Pasteur that his scientific enthusiasm was closely interwoven with his very earnest and sincere patriotism. Even of an academic problem awaiting solution he vehemently said, "It is a question that *France* should make it a point of honour to solve through one of her children." Each of his successful researches rejoiced him the more because it was made in France and for the honour and good of France. Knowledge once won is of no country; it is the common guerdon of mankind; but he who cares nothing as to where it grows seems to lack an element of patriotism. If from our land, rather than from another, should come, for instance, the knowledge that is ultimately to remove the terrible curse of cancer it would be a legitimate source of national pride. Just before the war there was established in connection with the National Insurance Act a considerable endowment for research in medicine—an entirely new departure in the policy of this country. The committee entrusted with the expenditure of the public moneys has in duty bound devoted its resources during the war to investigations called for by the war itself, and important work has been done of which the public has little cognisance. Afterwards, it is to be hoped, its resources may be strengthened rather than weakened.

It is not financial assistance alone, however, which the nation should provide for the investigator. This is not even the most important stimulus that the nation can provide for him. Recognition and proper standing in the body politic are his due, and these should be at last forthcoming.

# THE "SPECIFIC TREATMENT" OF DISEASE

By GEORGE H. F. NUTTALL, F.R.S.,

*Quick Professor of Biology in the University of Cambridge.*

Until recently medical men employed but few remedies which exerted a marked curative effect on particular infective diseases. Mercury is the drug which has been longest used as a "specific" remedy in the treatment of "specific disease," which is a name frequently applied by medical men to syphilis. This disease is an ancient scourge of the human race and its treatment by mercury dates far back into the past, iodide of potash having only in more recent times been added to the armamentarium of physicians who used it especially in the later stages of the malady. A second specific remedy is quinine, now universally used in the treatment of malaria. This drug is derived from cinchona bark which had long been in use by the natives of Peru before its introduction into Europe in the 17th century.

How it was discovered that mercury and cinchona bark exerted their particular curative effects

## PURE SCIENCE

it is impossible to say, but it is probable that some happy chance brought them into use. From what we see taking place around us at the present day we are justified in believing that myriads of men have in the past fallen victims to the ignorant who sought to apply all kinds of supposed remedies to the alleviation of their sufferings.

In the wild-goose chase for remedies in the past the result was generally negative and the physician had almost invariably to resign himself to do what he could through merely alleviating by the simplest means the most distressing symptoms of his patient. He resorted to what is called "palliative" or "symptomatic" treatment, that is he made his patient as comfortable as he could or he sought to abate distressing symptoms without pretending really to cure him, trusting the while to beneficent Nature to lend a helping hand where his strength failed.

We shall see how the blind hunt for remedies subsided and scientific method came to be introduced into investigations. Scientific research in the true sense aims at the acquisition of knowledge for its own sake, for it is indirectly through the advances in pure science that man has been rewarded by the greatest discoveries possessing a practical bearing. These advances have been rendered possible through work in many directions and it is by coordinating the knowledge acquired in different sciences that the best results have been attained. The object of pure science in any branch is to arrive at the truth as far as it is humanly possible, to study phenomena as objectively as we can without any thought of the applications to which the knowledge gained can be put. It is difficult to convince the narrow-minded "practical man," so happily self-confident is he, that a knowledge of useful things after all represents but a limited amount of knowledge. He jogs along the road of life like a horse with blinkers, with a view limited to what he sees in front of him—the practical result only. The function of the worker in pure science may be likened to that of a scout in the army who goes out to gather all the information he can, and to do this effectively he must keep his mind, his eyes, and every sense open. The "practical man" tries to be a scout, but the blinkers which he wears confine his field of observation and lead him frequently into absurd errors. It is unfortunate for this country that these blinker-wearers, who persistently deny that they wear blinkers, have so much to say in educational matters. It is hoped that with time the public will realize the difference between pure science and applied science and do their duty in furthering the former which leads the way to discovery and progress.

Although scientific minds have influenced human thought in the past and led to important discoveries it is only in modern times that science has really begun to flourish. We live in the age of science, of science applied and, as we see in the present war, of science misapplied. It is the object of this short essay to trace the origin and rise of scientific method in a limited domain of knowledge and to show what may be the fruits of labour wisely guided.

### THE RISE OF MODERN PATHOLOGY.

Anatomy, one of the oldest sciences allied to medicine, concerns itself with the structure of the body and the mechanism of its component parts. Already at an early date, anatomists reached definite conclusions regarding the position of various organs and their general structure and function. By studying the joints and determining, for instance, the points of origin and insertion of the muscles upon the skeleton, students acquired a fair knowledge of the mechanism of locomotion. Efforts were soon made to explain the functions of certain organs of the body. Many sought to explain what they or others had observed by resorting to a process of reasoning that frequently led to absurd conclusions, for the imagination was allowed to run riot.

The respect for authority dominated the Christian Church and this reacted adversely upon original research, for the church dominated learning. The works of classical writers became for centuries the bible of anatomists and physicians. The revolt began with the renaissance and an epoch was marked by the publication in 1543 of Vesalius's *Fabrica Humani Corporis*. This author, a Belgian, taught surgery and anatomy in Padua. Finding the classical authors constantly in error he cast them out and taught his pupils only *what he could himself see and demonstrate to others*. Nevertheless, it was not until 1628 that William Harvey demonstrated the circulation of the blood, while the study of the functions of other organs was only attacked at a later date. As time progressed it became clearer that the only way of studying the processes which take place in the body was by the experimental method and, failing man as a subject, by resorting to the study of these processes in living animals.

Physiology concerns itself with the functions of all the organs of the body and the processes that take place in them in health. Though much anatomy can be learnt from dead bodies this does not hold for physiology. To study what takes place in the living body it is necessary to subject the living to experiment. As man is similar to a number of animals in certain essential points of structure and function, it was natural that recourse was had to animals for the study of those functions which could not be investigated in man. When we survey the knowledge acquired in the domain of physiology we are compelled to realize that practically all the progress that has been made in

# THE RISE OF PATHOLOGY

this field is based on experimental research conducted in animals. By physiological research in animals we have gained a profounder knowledge of the functions of the nervous system, of the process of repair in tissues, of the functions of the various glands, of the processes of digestion and functions of the heart and of the circulatory and respiratory systems. Modern medicine and surgery are largely based on the knowledge gained in physiological laboratories.

The rise of pathology to the rank of a science is comparatively recent. The physiologist having paved the way by giving us a sound knowledge of many of the functions of the body in health, medical men were better prepared to gain an insight into the processes of disease, for it is with these processes that pathology deals, besides the cause of disease and its effects. The earlier work on pathology concerned itself mainly with the naked eye appearances presented by the organs of those that had died of disease. The anatomical and pathological examination of the bodies of the dead was frequently conducted with difficulty and in the face of opposition from the hand of the law and public opinion which forbade any tampering with the human cadaver. Consequently these examinations were usually made in secret on exhumed bodies and no records were kept. At most a few favoured pupils of the early pathologist gathered a smattering of knowledge from the hurried observations of the master. It is evident that pathological observation limited to the naked eye examination of the organs of the dead could throw little or no light upon the processes of disease although they may show us some of the consequences.

Men had long been asking themselves what constitutes disease, relapse, cure and recovery, natural and acquired immunity; is disease merely due to disordered function or to some outside cause? With the discovery of the microscope, which taught men to look at things more carefully, and the adoption of the experimental method of investigation by many inquirers, the light began to dawn.

Long experience had demonstrated that certain diseases were communicated from one individual to another and such maladies were classed by themselves. It is mainly with these that we shall concern ourselves, as it is chiefly in relation to infective diseases that progress has been made. It was long suspected by some acute observers that infective diseases were due to the entrance into the body of parasites which multiplied therein and were given off by the sick to their surroundings; an indication of something of the kind being afforded by what had been observed in the case of larger parasites and their effects.

In the last century, Louis Pasteur, a French chemist, undertook the study of the fermentation processes that take place in the manufacture of wine, the object being to ascertain why certain wines deteriorated and others did not. In due course he discovered that the wines were spoiled by the entrance into them of microorganisms (yeasts, etc.) that produced fermentations of an unsuitable kind accompanied by flavours which did not suit the tastes of the consumers. This discovery of the causes of so-called "diseases of wines" was of far-reaching importance, as it started a line of reasoning in Pasteur's mind which led him to assume that animal diseases might similarly be due to the multiplication of microorganisms in the body. Some years before, microscopic rod-like vegetable organisms, which are known to-day as bacilli, had been found by Davaine multiplying in the blood of cattle suffering from anthrax. Pasteur explained the significance of these anthrax bacilli: he showed that they were the cause of the disease so fatal to sheep and cattle, also affecting human beings, especially persons dealing with sheeps' wool and the skins and other products of animals which had died from anthrax. Jenner had demonstrated long before that protection is afforded against smallpox—an affection which is communicable by inoculation—by vaccine obtained from the calf. The vaccine produced a mild disease which after recovery afforded protection. It was assumed that the smallpox virus had become attenuated or lowered in virulence by passage through the body of the calf. Pasteur, with this observation in mind, sought to lower the virulence of the anthrax bacillus which he had learnt to cultivate in suitable media in the laboratory. By prolonged cultivation of the bacilli at temperatures higher than those at which they grew luxuriantly, he succeeded in grading their virulence. Whereas the original stock of bacilli, even in very small doses, was fatal for sheep inoculated with it, he found that the cultures grown at high temperatures exerted no such effect. The most attenuated (1st vaccine) only killed highly susceptible mice slowly, the less attenuated (2nd vaccine) killed mice and rabbits, and usually had but a slight effect on sheep. Pasteur found that by inoculating sheep with the 1st vaccine, followed after some days by the 2nd vaccine, he could render the sheep resistant against inoculation with fully virulent strains of bacilli. These observations, followed by those of many other workers, on different diseases led to results of immense practical importance. Lister, in England, applied the discoveries of Pasteur to the prevention of wound infection with results that ushered in a revolution in surgical methods which has benefited man throughout the world by saving untold thousands of lives.

In the years that followed, the impulse given by Pasteur was seen at work in different countries. Pasteur had made discoveries on the disease of silkworms in France, on septicemia in fowls and

# METCHNIKOFF

other diseases. In Germany, Robert Koch, after discovering the bacillus of tuberculosis, confirmed and extended the work of Pasteur on anthrax. Koch or his disciples discovered the cause of cholera, enteric fever, lock-jaw, dipththeria, glanders, etc. Pasteur made discoveries of fundamental importance in relation to hydrophobia and its treatment which have resulted in the saving of innumerable lives. Whilst omitting minor discoveries we may add that Bruce, working in Malta, discovered the cause of undulant fever.

Meanwhile the eminent Russian zoologist Metchnikoff, when studying small fresh-water crustacea known as Daphnia, observed that they were parasitized by microorganisms which were frequently engulfed by the wandering cells in their body cavities. He next studied the behaviour of anthrax bacilli in the body of the frog, an animal which under ordinary conditions is resistant to infection with this microorganism. He observed that the bacilli soon after their introduction beneath the animal's skin were taken up by the frog's wandering cells or leucocytes after which they degenerated and died. Metchnikoff next advanced a fascinating explanation of these phenomena. He regarded the wandering cell in the animal economy as a cell having varied functions, amongst others that of defending the body against invasion by the germs of disease. He drew a graphic picture of the wandering cells (to which he gave the name of phagocytes) seizing and digesting the offending intruder, and he likened their increase in the blood to the gathering of soldiers to meet invasion. According to Metchnikoff, then, the resistance of an animal to infection depends upon the power of its wandering cells to take up and digest the intruding microorganism. "Metchnikoff's phagocyte theory," as it was called, gained many adherents, for it offered what appeared to be a tangible explanation and it was defended with much ingenuity and persistence by its author. We shall see that the view propounded by Metchnikoff has undergone considerable modification although the term "phagocytosis" has firmly established itself in the terminology of biologists and pathologists for the phenomena he observed. Metchnikoff's views gave rise to active controversies which greatly stimulated research into the phenomena of immunity and disease.

Whilst carrying on research in Flügge's laboratory in 1886, the writer resolved to repeat the classical experiments of Metchnikoff upon the frog and anthrax bacilli. He observed the identical phenomena recorded by Metchnikoff, but he was led to put an entirely different interpretation upon them—for he found that the bacilli rapidly degenerated and died in the fresh blood of the frog without the intervention of wandering cells. The explanation offered was that the cells take up bacilli that are degenerating and dying owing to the bacteria-killing power of the frog's blood, fluid or

## TOXINS AND ANTITOXINS 267

serum, without the intervention of "phagocytes." The fresh serum of other animals was next studied and found to possess great bactericidal power, in certain cases even in animals that were susceptible to thrax infection. These results pointed to the defensive mechanism being mainly situated in the fluids of the body and formed the basis of the "humoural theory" as against the "phagocyte theory." Nevertheless, it was clear that the composition of the serum is dependent primarily on the activities of the different kinds of cells which collectively constitute the body of an animal. These experiments are referred to because they formed the starting-point for researches which resulted in the discovery of the curative properties of serum, of "serum therapeutics." When it had been found that bacteria could be destroyed by serum the next step followed naturally, it was to try if the serum of an animal which had recovered from a disease possessed protective and curative properties when injected into an otherwise susceptible animal.

It is an old observation that persons by repeated dosing may attain a considerable tolerance to poisons and in certain cases may acquire a positive resistance to large doses of poisons which would otherwise cause death. It was found by Behring that the poison formed by the bacilli of diphtheria (or tetanus) in laboratory cultures if injected, in gradually increasing doses, into susceptible animals produced an enormously increased resistance to these poisons. When the serum of such resistant animals was injected into experimentally infected animals it was found to exert a curative effect. By raising the resistance of an animal to a high degree, rendering it hyper-immune, it was found that its serum possessed a considerable protective and curative power. The bacterial poisons are spoken of as toxins and the serum of the hyper-immunized animals as antitoxins. By a toxin we understand a poison of vegetable or animal origin whose exact chemical composition is unknown because of its complexity. A number of toxins are known besides those derived from bacteria: toxins for instance occur in the castor-oil bean and in the venom of snakes, spiders and scorpions. These toxins are only neutralized by their *specific* antitoxins, that is diphtheria antitoxin only neutralizes diphtheria toxin, tetanus antitoxin only neutralizes tetanus toxin, etc. When a toxin and its corresponding antitoxin are mixed in the test-tube in suitable proportions, the mixture is found to be harmless because the toxin is neutralized by the antitoxin present in the serum.

The practical results of these discoveries have been of immense value; in diphtheria alone in all its forms the mortality has been reduced from about 30% to 8% in practice. The antitoxin for tetanus is chiefly used in preventive treatment, being administered to persons (or horses) who have

## TOXINS AND ANTITOXINS 269

received wounds which may, if left untreated, give rise to lockjaw. Tetanus antiserum has been used on an unprecedented scale in the present war and has saved the lives of innumerable soldiers.

The study of the mode of action of antitoxin upon toxin in the test-tube and in the animal body has been fraught with difficulties because modern chemistry is still incapable of explaining the complex composition of the substances which act upon each other. There have been various attempts to explain the phenomena involved, and the explanation which has perhaps afforded the best working hypothesis and certainly most stimulated research is that of Ehrlich. According to this author the antitoxins are the products of the living cells of the body which have reacted to the stimulus of a corresponding toxin. A toxin is only capable of producing disease in individuals whose body cells contain substances capable of entering into chemical combination with the particular toxin. The toxin upon entering the body is taken up by these substances (called receptors); the cells react and produce receptors in excess so that they are thrown off into the blood stream, rendering the serum antitoxic. The receptors in the blood prevent the toxin from reaching the susceptible cells. Or, as Behring expresses it, the substance in the cell which makes it susceptible to the effects of toxin is the causative factor in recovery.

Apart from the antitoxins the body is capable

of producing other "anti-bodies" which neutralize injurious agents other than toxins; of these we may mention the bacteriolysins that kill and dissolve bacteria which invade the system. The antitoxins only neutralize the toxins. The formation of bacteriolysins occurs in a similar way to that of the antitoxins and they are likewise specific in character. As examples may be cited those contained in the serum of persons who have been rendered immune to cholera or typhoid fever where the bacteriolysins destroy the bacteria of cholera and typhoid respectively but exert no effect on other microorganisms.

The foregoing investigations and discoveries were the outcome of research by many investigators in laboratories in different parts of the world. A clearer conception arose as to the nature of acquired immunity and recovery in infective disease, and the complex character of the phenomena was also more appreciated.

The next step in advance was along the lines of drug treatment in diseases such as sleeping sickness which are due to Protozoa, the lowest forms of animal life. It had long been known to those who used the microscope in the study of the minute anatomy or histology of animals and plants that the cells of which their tissues and organs were composed showed a peculiar behaviour towards dyes of various kinds. Whereas the cells or parts of cells of one organ in an animal could be successfully stained by a given dye, the cells of some other organ in the same animal reacted differently to the dye. In other words some dyes showed what is known as a selective affinity for certain cells. These dyes were used in the study of dead tissues. As time went on it was found that certain aniline dyes, in high dilution, exerted but a slight or no observably injurious effect on living cells, whilst a certain amount of the colouring matter was absorbed into the living tissue. Such staining of living cells became known as intra-vital staining and it served many a useful purpose in the laboratory. Ehrlich, continuing his studies on immunity, was struck by this phenomenon and its possible bearing upon the action of drugs in the body. Dilute methylene blue for instance had been found to produce intra-vital staining in nerve tissue. Ehrlich argued that this power to take up certain substances like dyes afforded an indication that the cells of the body might take up drugs in a similar manner. The drug might augment the natural resisting power of the body when it reacted to the stimulus of the invading parasite or the drug might show a selective and more directly injurious action upon the microorganism itself. He began by studying blood parasites which cause trypanosomiasis, a group name for diseases in vertebrate animals of which sleeping sickness in man may be taken as an example. He discovered an aniline dye to which he gave the name of trypan-red because he found that it had a remarkable effect on the trypanosomes which cause this group of diseases. When injected into animals harbouring millions of trypanosomes in their blood, it was found that the parasites quickly disappeared and the animals showed rapid recovery. The recovery was, however, brief, for after a while the trypanosomes reappeared and it was found that with time they had grown resistant to the dye. These results gave promise and supported the view advanced by Ehrlich that by logically conducted research specific remedies might be found for the various specific diseases. He tested a vast array of substances and found a few which exerted an appreciable effect, and by unremitting toil scored some brilliant successes to which we shall presently refer.

Meanwhile, in France, another dye to which Mesnil gave the name of trypan-blue had been found to have an advantage over trypan-red in that it produced much less injurious local effects when injected into experimental animals suffering from trypanosomiasis. It was found, however, not to effect a permanent cure, and was abandoned in favour of the better treatment subsequently discovered by Ehrlich.

Trypan-blue was found by Nuttall and Hadwen to be a very useful remedy for another group of protozoal diseases. In cattle, horses, sheep and dogs there occur affections which may be broadly compared to malaria in man, since the

## PIROPLASMOSIS

minute protozoal parasites causing them live and multiply in the red blood corpuscles of the animals. This "malaria" in animals is known as piroplasmosis, but the parasites differ in each of the hosts named. The parasite for instance which occurs in cattle is not capable of producing infection in sheep, horses and dogs, and *vice versa*. Whereas malaria is conveyed by the bites of infected mosquitoes piroplasmosis is conveyed by infected ticks.

Piroplasmosis causes a heavy mortality in animals; it may entirely destroy large herds of cattle, and before the discovery of the remedy referred to it was impossible to keep dogs in many parts of Africa. Piroplasmosis or red-water, as it is frequently called, is a scourge of all the great cattle-raising areas of the world. Trypan-blue constitutes the only drug hitherto found of practical use in the treatment of piroplasmosis; it has been successfully used for some years in the treatment of dogs, horses and cattle. The curative effects in the dog are impressive to witness—an animal with high fever and almost dying will show marked outward signs of recovery within an hour or two. In untreated dogs the mortality is almost 100 %; in dogs receiving early treatment the recovery is practically about 90 %.

Ehrlich, finding the dyes ineffective in the treatment of trypanosomiasis, experimented with other compounds, notably with those containing arsenic, a substance which has long been used in medicine in small doses. He discovered a compound called Atoxyl, which exerted a marked effect on the parasites of sleeping sickness and which has been largely used in practice. There are drawbacks and dangers to its use, a drawback being that the trypanosomes become arsenic-resistant and other remedies such as tartar emetic have to be subsequently used to alleviate the patient. There is no doubt that these drugs prolong the life of persons suffering from sleeping sickness in its early stages and that they may help the body to throw off the infection. Unfortunately trypanosomiasis may last for years, and cases have been observed where apparently cured persons have suffered from a fatal return of the disease a year or two after they were treated. It is clear, therefore, that the ideal remedy still requires to be found. The results obtained are, however, full of promise for the future. In the meantime efforts have been made to lessen the chances of man's becoming infected by attacking the haunts of the tse-tse flies which convey the disease; the excellent results obtained in combatting the mosquitoes which convey malaria and yellow fever and the ticks which convey piroplasmosis having aroused hopes that similar measures directed against tse-tse flies might yield good results.

The most striking results obtained have been those in the diagnosis and treatment of syphilis, and we **may** consider the steps which have led to these discoveries. Although syphilis has been known

## SYPHILIS

from a remote period to be a disease which is communicable from man to man by infective secretions, the earlier efforts to gain a deeper insight into its nature by experimental infection of animals gave either negative or doubtful results. In 1903 Metchnikoff and Roux, in Paris, for the first time reproduced the typical effects of primary and secondary syphilis in apes (chimpanzees and ourang outangs) which they inoculated with infective material obtained from syphilitic persons. They subsequently reproduced the disease in apes by means of the semen of syphilitic subjects and demonstrated that the organs of persons suffering from the final or tertiary form of the disease still harboured the virus. This was of special interest, since tertiary syphilis was usually regarded as noninfective until these observers proved the contrary. In 1905 Schaudinn, a German zoologist, discovered the microorganism which is the cause of this dread disease, a very minute spiral organism which, owing to its small size and the difficulty of seeing it because of its optical properties and resistance to stains, had escaped the observation of many acute observers who in previous decades had searched for the causative agent of syphilis. This microorganism is known as the *Spirochaeta pallida*, and its discovery has proved of very great practical utility. The search for it is now commonly conducted by means of an instrument known as an ultramicroscope which reveals the spirochaetes as actively swimming spiral threads upon a dark background. The presence of spirochaetes in the primary sore of syphilis, in the secondary skin eruption, and in the tissues of persons affected by tertiary syphilis, is of positive value in diagnosing the disease. It ensures the *early* diagnosis of the disease and prompt recourse to treatment. Apart from this a most useful means of diagnosis based on similar work by other observers was introduced by Wassermann; this is known as the "complement deviation test," but a description of the test need not be considered here, since it would lead the reader too far afield.

The discovery that syphilis is communicable to animals, coupled with a knowledge of the character of the infective spirochaete, at once gave hope of a rapid advance in the study of the disease. Although syphilis had doubtless been experimentally produced in monkeys and even in rabbits before the date of these discoveries, the mild and atypical effects observed could not be certainly determined as representing true syphilis. The discovery of the spirochaete changed this completely by rendering diagnosis certain.

At this point Ehrlich threw himself into the study of syphilis and sought to find a cure for the disease experimentally induced in animals. In due course he found a remedy in an arsenical compound which became known as "606" or "salvarsan." Similar drugs are now manufactured in different countries under various names which need not be enumerated. Having found that salvarsan cured syphilis in animals the next step consisted in testing the effects of the drug on man, several German professors submitting themselves to being dosed with the drug without harmful consequences. Finally the drug was tested on syphilitic men, with brilliant results which have since led to its adoption in the treatment of this dread disease throughout the world.

We come finally to the remarkable curative effects of salvarsan which Ehrlich discovered in relapsing fever. This disease occurs among people living in filth and neglect, and it has been demonstrated that it is transmitted by the bites of lice which have previously sucked the blood of the sick. In past times as in the present relapsing fever has been a scourge of armies in the field, for soldiers on campaign commonly become verminous. The cause of the disease is a minute spirochaete, differing somewhat from that of syphilis and multiplying in the blood. The disease, as its name implies, is characterized by periodic attacks of fever or relapses which correspond with the appearance in the blood of enormous swarms of actively moving spirochaetes which disappear with the subsidence of each attack. Relapsing fever is not usually a very fatal disease, the death-rate generally averages 4% but it may be greater. The seriousness of the disease is due to the long period of invalidism which may follow. The heart may be so weakened as to lead to death from heart failure on slight exertion, and death may follow from other causes operating upon the weakened individual. There are usually three relapses in the course of the disease, but there may be fewer or more. In a patient whose blood is swarming with spirochaetes and who is in high fever the injection of a single dose of salvarsan is immediate in its action. The spirochaetes begin to disappear almost at once, the fever ceases and the patient recovers promptly.

Although much has been omitted in the foregoing account, because for obvious reasons it is impossible to go into details, it is hoped that the reader, who is not already familiar with the subject, will have gathered this impression:

That the dawn of modern medicine coincided with the introduction of scientific experimental method and observation into the study of the processes taking place in the body in health and disease.

That every great advance has been purchased by the unremitting toil of many laboratory workers who have sought to discover the truth for its own sake.

That knowledge acquired in all branches of pure science may in the ripeness of time render the greatest practical service to man.

# FLIES AND DISEASE

## By G. S. Graham-Smith, M.D.
*University Lecturer in Hygiene in the University of Cambridge.*

Most people probably regard Entomology, or the study of insects, as an interesting hobby followed by a few enthusiasts who collect and examine specimens and recount fascinating tales of the lives of many curious creatures. The earlier students no doubt were actuated only by love for their special subject, but for many years the economic importance of insects has been recognized and their habits have been studied in relation to Agriculture, Forestry and many other subjects.

Within the last forty years it has been shown that insects, and especially flies, are important agents in transmitting many serious and widespread diseases both to men and to animals. These discoveries are among the most important in medical science within modern times, and have led to far-reaching results.

Once the causative microbe of a disease and its mode of transmission are known, medical science aims rather at the prevention of the scourge than at the cure of individuals. Few appreciate the remarkable achievements already attained in controlling and eradicating some of the most deadly pestilences. Success in controlling an epidemic disease transmitted by the agency of insects depends on a thorough knowledge of the various factors concerned in its production: the life-history of the causative parasite in man; the periods during which he is capable of infecting the insect carrier; the influence of drugs on the parasite while in the human body; the relationship of the parasite to the transmitting insects; the life-histories of the insects and their habits under various conditions; and the influence of climate, locality, etc., on the patients, the parasites and the insects.

In regard to most diseases the necessary knowledge can be acquired only by slow degrees. First the disease is separated from others which resemble it by careful analyses of the symptoms prevailing in various outbreaks. In time it is recognized that patients exhibiting certain groups of symptoms are suffering from a definite disease, which is probably caused by a certain kind of microorganism. Until considerable advances in bacteriology had been made the identification of some infectious diseases, and especially of the less common forms of these diseases, was very uncertain. Not only have bacteriology, concerned mainly with those minute forms of life, which are regarded as vegetable in type, and the allied science of protozoology, which deals with the minute forms, which are regarded as animal in type, rendered immense aid to medicine in making the diagnoses of infectious diseases more certain and elucidating the processes which occur in patients suffering from them, but they have widened the very narrow views previously held. We now know that an individual infected with a certain disease-producing microorganism, for example the diphtheria bacillus, may exhibit a great variety of symptoms. He may suffer from the disease in an acute form and die in a few hours or days, or he may suffer from the disease in a subacute or mild form, showing the typical symptoms in a lesser degree. Such conditions are easily recognizable and give rise to few difficulties in diagnosis. The patients are isolated, and at least for a time are prevented from spreading the disease. Many individuals, who become infected, exhibit symptoms which are less easily recognizable, such as mild sore throats, nasal catarrh, etc., while others, though harbouring the bacilli, remain in perfect health. Such persons are known as 'carriers,' and are of the greatest importance. They can be recognized only by bacteriological examination; they frequently remain undetected and go about unconsciously spreading infection. Further, those who have recovered from the disease in its recognizable forms frequently harbour the bacilli for long periods and disseminate infection as do the carriers. Every infectious disease has its typical, atypical, mild cases, and carriers, and it is on the recognition of this fact that the modern measures for the control of such diseases have been founded.

The minute parasites which cause disease may be divided into three classes, the bacteria, the protozoa and the ultra-microscopic organisms.

Innumerable organisms belonging to all three classes exist, but only a small proportion of them are in any way connected with disease, the majority performing various other functions in the economy of nature. Several species of bacteria produce diseases of different kinds, some when they gain entrance into the intestinal tract and others when they invade the tissues. In most bacterial diseases the organisms are conveyed directly from a patient or carrier to a healthy person, while in some these organisms may be conveyed in milk, water, food, or by insects, and certain species, which are present in the soil, are apt to infect wounds. Bacteria multiply by division when they find conditions suitable for their growth and exhibit no complicated phases in their life-cycles. Most species of disease-producing bacteria are easily killed by exposure to light and by drying, and apparently do not survive very long outside the bodies of men or animals. A few species however are more resistant, especially such as are capable of forming spores. So far as we know at present most disease-producing bacteria do not multiply in the bodies of insects, or live in them for more than a few days. In regard to bacteria, therefore, flies only act as mechanical carriers of organisms, which they may take up on their feet or in their intestines from infected sources, and deposit them on human food or on the surfaces of wounds. In studying the conveyance of bacteria by flies we have therefore to consider two main problems, the possible sources from which the insects can obtain infective material, and the habits of the flies in relation to the distribution of the bacteria they have acquired.

Many of the disease-producing protozoa pass certain portions of their lives in the blood of the infected persons, and infection is usually brought about by the direct injection of these organisms under the skin by the bites of infected insects. In this class of organism the life-cycle is often most complicated, a cycle of multiplication by simple division within the human body being followed by a complex sexual cycle in the insect carrier. In these cases the cycle within the insect is a very important and in fact an essential part in the life-history of the protozoon, and the fly cannot be regarded as a mechanical carrier only.

The ultra-microscopic organisms are too small to be seen distinctly under the highest powers of the microscope, but in some cases they undoubtedly behave in the same manner as the protozoa.

In such diseases it follows that if the fly can be prevented from biting the patient, or if the flies can be destroyed, the spread of the disease will be prevented.

In the case of insect-borne protozoal diseases several factors have to be taken into consideration; the periods of their life-cycle in the human body when the parasites are so distributed that biting insects can become infected; the actions of drugs on the parasites; the life-cycles of the parasites in the insects, and the periods when the insects are capable of causing infection; and lastly the habits of the insects. Also it must be borne in mind that certain animals may act as reservoirs of infection for the flies, becoming infected with the parasites and harbouring them for long periods, but showing no signs of disease, and further that protozoa of many diseases can only complete their life-cycles in certain species of flies.

Considered as carriers of disease-producing organisms flies may be divided into two classes, (1) those in which the proboscis is constructed in such a manner as to be capable of piercing the skin—blood-sucking flies, and (2) those in which the proboscis is so constructed as to be incapable of piercing the skin—non-blood-sucking flies. The former live mainly on blood, while the latter live on various liquid foods.

## Organisms Transmitted by Blood-sucking Flies.

The discovery, which first clearly demonstrated that flies may act as carriers of parasitic micro-organisms, was made by Manson in 1878. It had been known for several years previous to this date that in China and other tropical countries the young stages of a small parasitic worm, known as *Filaria bancrofti*, were present in the blood of some individuals. These young worms are the progeny of parents living in the internal organs. Sometimes they are present in the blood during the day and disappear at night, and in other patients the reverse is the case. For further development the young worms require to be ingested by a mosquito, when the latter is sucking the blood of the patient. The young worm soon bores its way out of the stomach into the muscles of the mosquito, where it passes through various stages in its development. About the eighth day the worms make their way into the proboscis of the mosquito and remain there till the mosquito bites a man, when they pass out onto the skin through which they bore and make their way into his body.

A similar disease of dogs is transmitted in the same way.

The investigations on Yellow Fever may be quoted at some length for several reasons. The disease is a most important one in the regions in which it occurs and is of particular interest because it is caused by an ultra-microscopic organism. Further the researches which elucidated its cause and mode of transmission show how difficulties, which at first appear insuperable, may be overcome, and lastly the measures for the limitation of this disease founded on these researches have been attended with very remarkable results.

The disease is widely distributed in tropical and subtropical America, also, according to most authorities, on the West Coast of Africa. In early times it was believed that the virus was in some way transmitted through the air, and later several species of bacteria were described as the cause of the disease. The disease was considered to be highly contagious; patients suffering from it were strictly isolated and their clothing, etc. thoroughly sterilized. In spite of the isolation of patients, however, epidemics were not checked and it was noticed that many persons became infected without ever having come into contact with cases, whilst frequently doctors and nurses, who worked in the same rooms as the patients, did not suffer from it. Mosquitoes were suspected as early as 1848, but the cause and mode of infection remained obscure until the disease was studied in Cuba by an American Commission in 1899.

The Commissioners first investigated the claims made for various bacteria and showed that none of these were the cause of the disease. As it was generally held that the vomit and excreta of patients were very infectious the Commissioners next devoted their attention to the elucidation of this question. Since no animals were known to suffer from the disease it was necessary to find persons who were willing to offer themselves for experiment. Volunteers, who had never been in infected districts and were therefore not immune to the disease, were isolated in specially prepared, ill-ventilated and ill-lighted huts, and slept for days in beds freshly saturated with the discharges of yellow fever patients. Yet none of them became infected. By a series of such experiments the Commissioners showed that the common belief that these discharges were infectious was incorrect, and that the disease was not spread by such means. They next investigated the condition of the blood and ascertained that no bacteria were present in it. Nevertheless the blood, at least during the first three days of the illness, if injected in very small quantities into healthy persons causes the disease, and therefore some virus is present in it. This virus is so minute that it will pass easily through a porcelain filter capable of stopping all known bacteria. It is quickly killed by drying and is destroyed in five minutes by a temperature of 130° F. All these important facts had to be ascertained by the inoculation of healthy persons. By these researches the Commissioners showed that the causal agent was present in the blood, and it only remained to ascertain its mode of transmission. A common local mosquito, called *Stegomyia fasciata*, seemed to be the insect most likely to carry the disease, and experiments on persons who offered themselves were conducted with the most rigorous precautions against any external contamination. A house was constructed and rendered mosquito-proof by wire gauze, and divided into two halves by a partition of the same material. On the one side persons occupying the room slept between soiled bed-linen from yellow fever patients, etc. Into the other half only carefully sterilized material was allowed to enter, but in addition mosquitoes that had fed previously on yellow fever patients were introduced. A volunteer who entered this half of the house was bitten and shortly afterwards developed a typical attack of yellow fever, whilst persons who occupied the other half of the house for at least twenty days remained healthy.

By such experiments the important truth was established that yellow fever is only conveyed by means of mosquitoes. It was further shown that the mosquitoes only become infective twelve days after feeding on a patient, indicating that as in Malaria the parasite undergoes some developmental changes in the mosquito.

These facts once firmly established the Commissioners studied the life-history of the mosquito and based preventive measures on their researches.

## YELLOW FEVER

To check the spread of the disease it is necessary to prevent mosquitoes biting patients, and as far as possible to destroy the mosquitoes. In Havana, the place chosen for the first campaign against the disease, patients were confined in mosquito nets, and the breeding places of the mosquito, large and small collections of water, were removed or treated in various ways. The result was that within a few months the disease had ceased in Havana, a place in which it had claimed very numerous victims every year.

"In the Panama Canal zone, which used to be one of the worst endemic regions in Central America, as a result of anti-mosquito campaigns the number of cases of yellow fever was reduced so rapidly that within five years the disease had completely disappeared from this region."

As evidence of the losses formerly caused by this disease may be cited the fact that "the French army in Santo Domingo in 1798 out of a total strength of 25,000 lost over 22,000 from yellow fever and four years later out of a total of 40,000 it lost 20,000."

We may next consider two very important protozoal diseases, Malaria and Sleeping Sickness, which are responsible for much sickness and an enormous mortality annually.

The parasites of Malaria, of which there are at least three varieties, have two periods of multiplication in their life-cycles, one in the red blood corpuscles of man and the other in a mosquito.

When introduced into the blood by the bite of an infected mosquito the parasite is a very minute sickle-shaped body, which bores its way into a red blood corpuscle. As the parasite grows it feeds on the substance of the red blood corpuscle and gradually destroys it. When it has reached a certain size—about three-quarters the diameter of the red corpuscle—the parasite divides into a number of smaller bodies. Then the corpuscle bursts and the small parasites escape into the blood and attack other red blood corpuscles. By this means infection is carried from one corpuscle to another, and very rapidly millions of the blood corpuscles become infected. This is the so-called asexual form of multiplication. Together with the forms of the parasite just mentioned certain large forms, which are regarded as males and females, are produced in some of the blood corpuscles. These sexual forms cannot develop further in the blood, and if they remain there most of them soon die off. The sexual cycle is completed in the internal organs of those species of mosquito, *Anophelines*, which can transmit the infection. When such a mosquito feeds on the blood of a patient it swallows both asexual and sexual forms of the malaria parasite. The former are digested and destroyed by the stomach juices of the mosquito, but the latter develop and escape from the blood corpuscles in which they were previously confined. The male form divides up into several thin, very minute, eel-like fragments,

## MALARIA

which swim rapidly and penetrate into the female forms. A female, thus fertilized, bores its way through the stomach wall and grows to a considerable size in the surrounding tissues. Then the substance of the female divides up into a great number of minute, spindle-shaped bodies, many of which find their way into the salivary glands of the mosquito. When the infected mosquito feeds on a human subject these spindle-shaped bodies pass with the saliva into the blood and start the asexual cycle previously described.

In this disease it is man, and not the mosquito, who forms the chief reservoir of infection. A man once infected, even though no longer exposed to re-infection, may harbour the parasite for years.

Much has been done to diminish the prevalence of this disease by studying the life-histories of mosquitoes and applying suitable preventive measures to their breeding places, and by the use of nets and screens in preventing both the healthy and the infected from being bitten. Before measures can be applied with success it is almost always necessary to study very thoroughly the conditions prevailing in the locality, and to survey the whole area accurately. Quinine has a marked influence on the parasites in the body, and the use of this drug as a preventative and as a curative agent has had a very beneficial influence in the prevention of malaria.

The diseases hitherto discussed are transmitted

by mosquitoes, but the next important disease to be considered, Sleeping Sickness, is transmitted by a large blood-sucking fly, known as the Tse-tse fly. This disease, which is the cause of a very great annual mortality in parts of Africa, is due to a large protozoon parasite, known as a Trypanosome, which swims freely in the blood and multiplies by division. There is a periodic increase and decrease in the number of trypanosomes in the blood, and accordingly the infectivity of the patient for the fly varies. In the fly the parasite passes through certain developmental stages and eventually the insect is capable of infecting a man, when it feeds on him. One of the most important facts recently discovered in regard to Sleeping Sickness is that wild game, antelopes and reed-bucks, serve as a reservoir for the parasite, remaining infective for long periods without showing any signs of the disease.

The problem of preventing this disease is a peculiarly difficult one, and much has yet to be learnt in regard to the habits of the fly and of its natural enemies before the disease can be successfully dealt with in all the regions it affects. In certain restricted areas, for example the Island of Principe in the Gulf of Guinea, the measures for destroying the fly have been completely successful and the spread of the disease has been checked.

Blood-sucking flies of various kinds transmit several other species of disease-producing organisms to men and animals, and other blood-sucking insects and ticks are responsible for the spread of other diseases.

### Non-Blood-sucking Flies.

The case against the common non-blood-sucking flies is more difficult to prove. That their habits are filthy and that they are constantly contaminated with bacteria is only too certain, but the precise extent to which they are responsible for the spread of disease has yet to be ascertained. We may first consider their habits and the experimental evidence in regard to their capacity for carrying and distributing disease-producing bacteria, and then the evidence relating to the actual production of disease through their agency.

Most of the common flies pass through the following stages in their life-histories. The females lay eggs in large clusters in decaying animal matter or excrement, and maggots emerge from the eggs in the course of a day or two. The maggots burrow below the surface of their food and grow rapidly. In two to four weeks they have reached their largest size, and then migrate from the food and either burrow in the ground or seek a sheltered position in which to change into the condition known as the pupal stage. In this stage the maggot ceases to feed or move, becomes barrel-shaped and develops a tough brown covering. During the quiescent stage, which lasts a few days in summer, the maggot within its protective covering turns into the fly, and finally the adult fly emerges by rupturing the covering. At first the fly is soft and the wings are folded up close to the body, but soon the wings expand and the fly becomes hard and capable of flight. An adult fly never grows, but remains the same size during the whole of its life. The winter is generally passed in the pupal stage.

The adults feed on excrement and decaying bodies and visit, when opportunity offers, fruit and human food. In walking over many of the filthy substances to which they are attracted their feet become contaminated with putrefactive and other bacteria, and these may be carried to the human food on which they next settle. This, however, is not the only or the most important manner in which these insects infect food. When a fly sucks up liquid filth the greater part of it passes at first into its crop, a sac-like organ in which the food is stored until the fly is able at leisure to discharge it into its intestine. After a meal the fly usually regurgitates part of the contents of its crop and this vomited material is left wherever it may happen to settle. Further, if a fly wishes to dissolve such a substance as sugar or milk dried near the mouth of a jug it does so by vomiting the crop contents over it. Since the crop contents are usually greatly contaminated with bacteria, some of which may be disease-producing forms, the infection of human food by means of vomit is often very gross.

Experimentally it has been shown that flies can

carry on their feet and in their crops the bacteria of nearly all the important infectious diseases and distribute them. Further the flies are not affected by these bacteria.

In civilized countries, with efficient drainage and scavenging systems and suitable hospital accommodation for infectious patients, flies seldom obtain opportunities of acquiring and carrying the bacilli of typhoid fever, dysentery or other similar diseases. On the other hand evidence is accumulating to show that they are very important agents in the dissemination of epidemic diarrhoea, a disease which causes a very great annual mortality amongst children. In tropical countries it seems almost certain that they are responsible to some extent for the spread of ophthalmia, cholera and some other diseases.

On the other hand in war-time their opportunities for acquiring and spreading the bacilli of typhoid fever and allied diseases are almost unlimited, and many competent observers have thought that they are responsible for a not inconsiderable proportion of the sickness that prevails. A quotation from the report of the American Commission, which investigated the sanitary conditions prevailing during the Spanish-American War, may suffice to illustrate the importance of non-blood-sucking flies in war time.

"There is no doubt that air and sunlight kill infection, if given time, but their very access gives opportunities for the flies to do serious mischief as conveyers of fresh infection. In a few minutes they load themselves with the dejections of a dysenteric or typhoid patient, as yet not sick enough to be in hospital or under observation, and they carry the poison so taken up into the very midst of the food and water ready for the next meal. There is no long roundabout process involved. It is very plain and direct, and yet when thousands of lives are at stake in this way the danger passes unnoticed and the consequences are disastrous and seem mysterious until attention is directed to the point; when it becomes simple enough in all conscience.

In most places the water supply was good and was not responsible for the spread of the typhoid fever. This was effected, in the opinion of the members of the Commission, by the flies, which swarmed in all the camps, and devoted their attention impartially and alternately to the fœcal matter in the open and to the food of the troops.

These pests had inflicted greater losses upon American soldiers than the arms of Spain."

From this short survey of some of the important fly-borne diseases it will be seen that practical measures for their eradication and control, and even for the treatment of patients, depend almost entirely on knowledge acquired by scientific investigations. It may be of advantage therefore to look more closely into the means of acquiring the accurate knowledge, which is so essential.

## BACTERIOLOGICAL DIAGNOSIS

The modern methods of research are so elaborate and so complex that no single observer can hope to obtain an intimate working acquaintance with more than a small section of a special subject, though he should possess sufficient acquaintance with the literature of those subjects which border on his own to criticize usefully the work of others and to broaden his own horizon.

The bacteriologist, who investigates those bacteria which produce disease in man, devotes years to the accurate study of a certain group or groups of such organisms. A group of bacteria comprises many species, superficially resembling each other very closely, but differing in their actions. Some produce disease, others are harmless parasites, and others again may have no connection with living bodies. The typhoid-colon group, for example, includes hundreds of species, indistinguishable from each other under the microscope, but one species produces typhoid or enteric fever in man, another paratyphoid fever, another dysentery, another food-poisoning; and others are responsible for diseases of various kinds in animals, while others are constant, and perhaps necessary, inhabitants of the intestines of men and animals. Though these species are microscopically indistinguishable, they can be divided into subgroups by their methods of growth under artificial conditions. Thus subgroups containing typhoid bacilli and species culturally resembling them, dysentery bacilli and their allies, and so on are distinguishable. The species within these subgroups can be further differentiated by observing the reactions of the bacilli with blood, and finally by their actions on living animals.

This short account of a single bacterial group illustrates the difficulties encountered in determining with certainty the identity of a bacterial species. While the elaboration of new distinguishing methods facilitates the recognition of certain types, advances in knowledge in other directions tend to increase the difficulties.

The bacteriologist has not only to study the distribution, the powers of resistance and the life-histories of bacteria outside the body so as to be able to distinguish them, but he has to study a much more intricate and important subject, their actions and life-histories within the body, and their relation to disease and infection. It is unnecessary to attempt to explain the methods used in such researches, but enough has been said to show that such work can be undertaken with success only by specialists, and that even with special knowledge and care trustworthy and far reaching conclusions can seldom be arrived at without years of careful study.

The work of the protozoologist is on similar lines. He is aided by the fact that some species of the protozoa can be identified under the microscope, but he labours under the serious disadvantage that artificial cultivation of these organisms is difficult.

The work of these scientific investigators, the bacteriologist and the protozoologist, is the foundation on which the whole superstructure relating to the recognition, treatment, control and eradication of infective diseases rests. The work must be as trustworthy as the present methods permit and the conclusions based on it reached by sound reasoning, or the practical measures founded on scientific investigations will fail and the efforts of the sanitarians be discredited.

The 'specific' treatment of infectious diseases is dealt with in a special article, and here it will suffice to mention that several of these diseases are treated by means of special 'sera,' resulting from the researches of bacteriologists, and some by drugs, acting 'specifically' upon the parasites within the living body, drugs which have been investigated and in some cases prepared by purely scientific methods.

The relationships of the fly to the parasite and to the patient are problems which require for their elucidation the joint researches of investigators acquainted with the normal structures and functions of the external and internal organs of flies, medical men who treat the patients, and bacteriologists and protozoologists, who investigate the parasites. These investigators ascertain the conditions under which the patients or their excreta can infect flies, the life-histories of the parasites in the flies, and the times during which the flies are infective to man.

The protozoal parasites causing certain diseases appear to be capable of completing their development in certain species of flies only, even closely allied species being apparently unsuitable. The cause of this curious restriction is unknown, but the fact, which is well established, necessitates the cooperation of experts who have given special attention to the difficult problems of differentiating closely allied species of flies in different phases of their life-histories.

Once research has shown that particular species of flies are concerned in the transmission of certain disease-producing organisms, the habits and life-histories of these species are minutely investigated by those who have devoted special attention to this line of research. At first sight investigations on the habits of flies may seem relatively simple, but further acquaintance with the subject will show that ingenious methods, accurate observations, special training and skill are essential, if information of sufficient accuracy to be of practical value is to be obtained.

Finally, general practical measures based on the scientific findings and designed to arrest the spread of a disease have to be devised, and these measures, modified to suit the conditions of different localities, are put into practice by medical officers and administrators. In dealing with some diseases the measures adopted have met with complete success and in many instances the results have been most beneficial, but in others they have been less satisfactory than was anticipated. Even unsatisfactory results may be valuable, for they direct attention to factors in the spread of the disease which have been insufficiently studied and thus lead to researches, which may eventually so increase our knowledge of the processes involved in the production and transmission of the disease as to render its complete control practicable.

# THE GOVERNMENT OF SUBJECT PEOPLES

By W. H. R. RIVERS, F.R.S.

*Fellow of St John's College, Cambridge.*

There is one department of government in which the end of the war will probably find the British Empire confronted with new responsibilities as well as with the duty of meeting old responsibilities in new ways. Whatever may be the fate of the German colonies which have been conquered directly by the mother-country, there is little doubt that those subdued by the efforts of South Africa, Australia and New Zealand will become part of the Empire and will greatly increase the extent of territory already governed by the Dominions.

In meeting these responsibilities, both new and old, various sciences will be called upon for help. We can safely hope that our rulers will recognise the value of those sciences which will make our possessions more healthy and more productive. The object of this essay is to inquire how far science may be useful in the work of government itself, how the group of sciences classed together under the general heading of anthropology can point the way to the better government of the indigenous peoples both of the new possessions and of those for whose welfare we have already long been responsible.

Whenever one people assumes the management of another, three lines of action are possible. One is to wipe out the indigenous culture as completely as possible and govern the people in accordance with the ideas and institutions of their new rulers. The second line of action is to preserve the indigenous culture in its entirety and to attempt to govern the people in accordance with the ideas which have come down to them from their fathers. The third and intermediate course is to uphold the indigenous culture except where it conflicts with the moral and social ideals of the governing people.

It is not necessary to discuss the merits of these policies, for the last has for long been adopted by the British Empire and by all other modern civilised nations which have undertaken the government of savage and barbarous peoples. It is very unlikely that this decision, dictated by humanity and common sense, and justified by long experience, will ever be reversed. If either of the other policies were adopted anthropology would have little, if anything, to contribute towards the work of government, at any rate until the time came, as come it certainly would, when the policy broke down. The position of anthropology is very different in the case of the third policy. Whatever be the degree of interference with indigenous customs involved in this policy, knowledge of the culture to be modified is absolutely necessary if changes are to be made without serious injury to the moral and material welfare of the people. Before we can decide in any satisfactory manner whether a custom or institution is contrary to our standards of morality and justice, we must understand its nature as exactly as possible. Certain customs such as cannibalism, infanticide, head-hunting and the immolation of widows are so clearly contrary to generally accepted standards of morality that they have been prohibited wherever Britain rules; but usually it is only these more flagrant examples of conflict with our own standards which have been prohibited, while other customs and institutions, containing elements equally contrary to these standards, have been left alone because the evil has not lain on the surface, and has remained unknown to, and even unsuspected by, the rulers.

Far more important, however, than this persistence of cruel or immoral practices is the serious modification, and even destruction, of native custom and institution which constantly take place owing to ignorance on the part of rulers. The customs thus changed or destroyed are often highly salutary, and may rest on a morality as high as our own, and yet the rulers may themselves have taken the leading part in the work of destruction by decisions which would have been impossible if they had understood the conditions with which they were interfering.

In other cases customs may escape change because they lie so deeply beneath the surface that they do not attract the attention of the rulers and remain altogether outside their ken. Such customs may be of the utmost importance to the people and may even furnish the key to the proper understanding of their social life. Moreover, they may in no way conflict with European standards of morality, and yet their persistence may act as a definite hindrance to good government, merely because they are not understood and serve as a perennial source of misunderstanding and distrust.

The object of this essay is to illustrate some of the ways in which anthropological knowledge may prevent mistakes and help rulers to make use of the beneficial customs so often practised even by rude and apparently degraded peoples.

The tasks of the anthropologist fall under three heads: (i) the collection, description and classification of facts; (ii) the inquiry into the past history of customs and institutions thus recorded and described, and into the laws which govern the processes of growth and degeneration which this history reveals; (iii) the study of the instincts, sentiments and beliefs which underlie both the social conduct of the present time and the laws which govern the changes to which society has been subject in the course of its history.

In the present state of the science it is the first only of these tasks which has so far given results of any practical value, and it is with the work of the anthropologist in the recording and classification of social facts that this essay will be mainly occupied.

The value to the administrator of a knowledge of the social conduct of the people he has to govern would seem to be so obvious as to leave little to be said. It is necessary to begin by pointing out certain considerations which have prevented and still prevent the recognition of the value of scientific work in the art of government.

It is a widespread popular idea that the chief tasks of the anthropologist are the measurement of heads and the collection of curious or beautiful objects for museums. It is because these have been his main occupation in the past and are believed by so many to be his main business still that the practical value of anthropology is so little recognised. In recent years, however, the whole movement of interest, especially in our own country, has been away from the physical and material towards the psychological and social aspects of the life of Mankind. The main interest of the anthropologist to-day and the most active growing-points of his knowledge lie in the regions concerned with the structure and organisation of human society, with the political and economic relations of its constituent elements, and with the group of social processes we call Religion which, among most of the peoples of the earth, binds together into one complicated thread the manifold activities of social life. Whatever may have been the preoccupations of the anthropologist in the past, his chief interest to-day is in just those regions of human activity with which the art of Government is daily and intimately concerned.

A second reason for the failure to recognise the value of scientific work in the art of government is that the minds of rulers are already occupied with an organised body of knowledge, the fruit of the gradually acquired experience of those who have been concerned in the work of government in the past. It is in the satisfaction of rulers with this knowledge and in their failure to recognise its incompleteness, and even its too frequent falsity, that there lies the chief obstacle to the recognition of the value of science in their work.

The general acceptance of these incomplete and false bodies of knowledge concerning the cultures of subject peoples is due to certain well recognised characteristics partly of the subject peoples, partly of the rulers themselves.

The chief characteristic of savage or barbarous peoples which leads to the formation of such a body of false knowledge is the attitude of respect towards their rulers which makes them very loath to contradict or correct them. The mode of action of this attitude shows itself with especial definiteness in the case of language. The language which is used between a subject people and its rulers usually differs in pronunciation, vocabulary, and grammar from that which the people use in their intercourse with one another.

The usual history of the process by which such a distorted language comes into being is as follows: an early settler uses a native word or expression wrongly, but as the people do not like to correct him they adopt his word or expression when they speak to him though they know it to be wrong and do not use it among themselves. When by the repetition of such mistakes the first settler has come to use a large body of such incorrect expressions, he is joined by another who, according to the almost invariable custom of those who go to live among strange peoples, does not learn from the natives but from those of his own race whom he finds already settled in his new home. The incorrect usages of the first settler are thus passed on and perpetuated, and in the course of time there is produced a systematised form of language, subject to constant variations arising out of the mistakes and whims of individual persons, which is adopted by the rulers and becomes the accepted means of intercourse between them and the people they govern.

The process by which the traditional knowledge of rulers thus comes to differ from that of the people they rule is especially obvious and easy to follow in the case of language, but it applies just as definitely, though perhaps less obviously, through the whole range of culture. When the acts of European administrators are not purely arbitrary, they do not depend upon a correct knowledge of native customs and modes of thought but upon a strange hybrid growth which has come into existence for use between the people and their rulers, though the natives know perfectly well that it does not correspond with the systems of customs, inherited from their forefathers, which they still regard as right and proper and still follow whenever they are allowed to manage their own affairs.

The process I have sketched is perhaps a natural mechanism by which indigenous customs are modified as the result of the contact of peoples and the blending of cultures, but though it may be called "natural," it does not promote good government nor does it foster a healthy sentiment of respect towards rulers. It is not good that a people should daily see men, who hold themselves to belong to a superior race, believing firmly in a code of knowledge which every native knows to be only a mongrel version of the truth. It would greatly surprise many a white official who governs a subject people if he could hear the natives laughing at his mistakes, not in the good humoured way which meets one willing to learn, but with the touch of contempt which comes from the daily sight of people confident in their wisdom but yet persisting in gross mistakes, and with the more than touch of bitterness only too natural when these wrong notions lead to injustice and misunderstanding.

Still more important are the hypocrisy and double-dealing which are inevitably bred of such relations between rulers and ruled. No people can follow one code of conduct when dealing with their rulers and another code in their dealings with one another without suffering both morally and physically. There is no more potent source of the lack of interest in life which is the bane of subject peoples than the knowledge that they are being ruled by men who do not understand them and apparently do not try to understand.

I have now considered certain conditions which have helped to obstruct the recognition of the value of scientific knowledge in the art of government. Before I pass on to deal with certain special subjects to illustrate how this knowledge may be useful, I take this opportunity to point out one feature of lowly culture which makes interference with its customs an especially delicate matter.

If we compare a number of varieties of human culture we find that the lower we go in the scale, the more rude and apparently primitive the institutions of the people, the more closely are these institutions bound together, the more dependent are the different elements of culture upon one another. If, as is generally held, progress consists in specialisation of social function, in the gradually increasing application of the principle of division of labour, this result is such as we might expect. It may be, of course, that the greater interdependence of the different elements of savage culture is only apparent, but almost certainly it is more than this. The close dependence of one department of social life upon another is so great that interference with any department has consequences more immediate and far reaching than in the more developed and specialised varieties of culture.

In our own social life we are accustomed to distinguish clearly certain departments, such as religion, politics, economics, medicine, etc. The existence of mutual relations between these different departments is, of course, fully recognised by every student of society, but the advance in specialisation and the relatively high degree of independence are shown by the fact that every department has its own practitioners, who form independent social groups, while their rules of conduct in relation to their special occupations form separate and distinct bodies of social regulations. One who attempts to give a description of the activity of any one department finds no serious difficulty in doing so without trenching seriously upon the special province of another.

Among savage peoples such definite distinction is not possible. Departments of culture which we distinguish clearly are so inextricably interwoven that the describer of customs and institutions has the greatest difficulty in dividing his subjects into compartments and is liable to fall into serious error when he attempts to assign different elements of social life to those categories which we recognise so clearly among ourselves. This is shown with especial clearness in the imperfect development of the division of social function. It is not possible to distinguish the chief from the priest or the priest from the leech[1]. Those social functions which we have classed under the headings of government, religion, and medicine are performed by one set of persons and are often but different aspects of one set of social processes.

It is a commonplace of history that a reform designed to effect some special purpose has often had secondary and unforeseen consequences far more potent in changing the face of society than had been expected by the promoters of the reform. This result is, of course, due to the fact that among ourselves the interdependence of different elements of culture is greater than appears on the surface, greater than the politician or the social reformer suppose. But if interference with the relatively highly differentiated societies of modern civilisation has these secondary consequences, how much greater must they be in societies whose different elements are so closely interwoven as they are among savage peoples.

We know that the disintegrating influence of European settlements becomes the greater the lower

[1] For an example cf. *Lancet*, Jan. 15, 1916.

# COMPLEXITY OF SOCIAL LIFE

we go in the scale of culture, and it is largely through the greater interdependence of the different aspects of social life that this effect is produced. The administrator who prohibits head-hunting, regarding it merely as a special kind of warfare, will produce effects far greater than he anticipates if, as is usually the case, head-hunting is closely connected with the most sacred religious beliefs of the people and acts as the chief stimulus to the practice of many of their material arts. Similarly, one who abolishes secret societies because he holds them to be "hot-beds of superstition" will produce effects he had never anticipated if, as is often the case, these societies provide the basis of the whole economic system of the people and embody religious practices of the utmost importance to their material and moral welfare. There is probably no part of the world where such customs as head-hunting or such institutions as secret societies do not need suppression or modification. But it is one thing to destroy or modify in ignorance, and it is quite another thing to do so with a knowledge of the consequences which must inevitably follow these courses of action. In the one case there is arbitrarily swept out of existence all perhaps which makes the lives of the people worth living, and they rapidly sink into the apathy which is the sure precursor of their end, or their economical and moral systems are so shattered that they are only too ready to adopt the worst features of the "civilisation" to which they have become subject. In the other case, steps can be taken to supply new interests in place of those it has been necessary to destroy, or it may be possible to preserve those features of the indigenous institution which tend towards health and morality while its cruel or immoral features are abolished and the energies underlying them directed into more healthy channels.

I have considered certain reasons for the failure to recognise the value of scientific knowledge in the art of government and certain features of lowly culture which make interference with it a matter of especial delicacy and difficulty. I shall now consider two topics which are frequent subjects of misunderstanding, in order to illustrate how knowledge may be beneficial in preventing mistakes and in utilising the moral and social trends of the indigenous culture to the best advantage both of the people and their rulers.

There is no subject more frequently misunderstood by the rulers of savage peoples than chieftainship. When a ruler begins to deal with such peoples, he finds it convenient to have some individual person who can represent them. The first business of the ruler of a region newly brought under subjection is usually to discover who are the chiefs in order to use them as intermediaries in his transactions with the people.

The generally accepted idea of a chief is that he is a man who administers justice, punishes offences against morality or social custom, leads in war and conducts negotiations with neighbouring peoples. Many serious mistakes have been made in the past owing to the fact that among many peoples, hardly one of these functions falls to the lot of those whom the people regard as chiefs, *i.e.* as the most important members of the community. Among many peoples those who are called chiefs have no more part in the administration of justice or in negotiations with neighbouring peoples than any other member of the community. If they are prominent in these departments of social activity, it is because they are personalities independently of their chieftainship. Among many peoples the duties of chiefs are mainly religious, their most important social functions being the arrangement of ceremonies and the furnishing of feasts. The newly arrived ruler who seeks a chief as intermediary between himself and the people will, if he is ignorant of the nature of their chieftainship, probably follow one of two courses. He will either treat as a chief one of those whom the people themselves regard in this light and impose upon him functions to which he is wholly strange, for which perhaps he is quite unfitted. Or, and this is the more frequent case, he treats as a chief one whom the people do not regard, and never have regarded in this light, some man of superior address or intelligence who may combine these qualities with others which lead to the unscrupulous use of his new position to exploit his fellows for his own ends. Even if it should happen that the man chosen as chief by the ruler possesses the necessary probity to represent the people justly, there is all the difference in the world between action with knowledge so that the choice can be justified and action in total ignorance of the revolution which is being introduced into the traditional practices of the people. Even if the course adopted be that which would have been taken with full knowledge, the way in which it is carried out leaves a feeling of dissatisfaction and injustice which could have been wholly avoided if the action had been based upon knowledge instead of ignorance.

The failure of justice in such a case can be traced to ignorance of the all pervading part taken by religion in the regulation of the social life of savage and barbarous peoples. Not only will the indirect effect of such ignorance do harm by the production of a sense of injustice, but occasionally ignorance of the religious or magical aspects of chieftainship may have still more disastrous consequences. Thus, among the Nubas of southern Kordofan the chief is also the rain-maker, and it is believed that his rain-making powers will come to an end if he leaves the hill upon which he and his people dwell[1]. Formerly, when an official wished to deal with a community of the Nubas he camped at the foot of their hill and sent for the chief, thus forcing the people to choose between disobedience to their

[1] I owe this information to Prof. C. G. Seligman.

# KINSHIP 317

foreign rulers and the loss of supernatural powers which they believe to be essential to their welfare. Placed in such a dilemma it is not surprising that they have preferred to offend the temporal powers, thus bringing immediate disaster on themselves and serious trouble and expense to their rulers. With knowledge of the fact that the chief is a rain-maker who must not leave his hill, it would have been easy for the official either to visit the hill himself or use some other intermediary.

Another subject which may be taken to illustrate the effects of ignorance of the institutions of savage and barbarous peoples is that of relationship or kinship. Among most of the peoples of the earth social relations are regulated by means of a system of kinship so widely different from our own that their languages have no exact equivalents for any of our terms of relationship and they have no terms which can be used as the equivalents of ours. The most widely diffused system of the kind is that known as "classificatory" in which such a term as father is not used for one person, but denotes a large class of relatives whom we distinguish from one another as father, uncle, first cousin once removed or still more distant relatives. There is a similarly wide use of mother, brother, sister and other terms which among ourselves are limited to a single person or to a small group of near relatives. Moreover, these terms are not mere modes of address but are associated with complicated systems of social privileges and obligations which make them of the utmost importance in the regulation of social life. The satisfactory settlement of disputes concerning the acquisition and transmission of property, and those arising out of land-tenure, marriage, divorce, etc., is impossible without a knowledge of these systems of relationship. Until lately the problems connected with relationship have been but little studied and have been widely misunderstood even by professed anthropologists, while they have been almost wholly ignored by administrators. I have myself been told by a magistrate of special experience and knowledge that in the courts he always passed over as quickly as possible questions involving a knowledge of relationship, and this was in a place where the social obligations connected with relationship are perhaps more important than in any other country with which we are acquainted.

Among ourselves the social obligations connected with relationship are relatively so few and simple that it is difficult adequately to illustrate the enormity of such ignorance. It may be feebly realised if we imagine England being governed by an alien people who are trying to administer justice in accordance with our own laws and institutions, but yet do not take the trouble to ascertain the meaning of such terms as father and son, and suppose them to apply to classes of persons as wide as those of the classificatory system. Small wonder that people thus treated should show no interest in life or in such management of their own affairs as is still left to them, and should be rapidly disappearing from the face of the earth.

The classificatory system is but one expression of a condition of communism or collectivism which, either in its complete form or as survivals of various degrees, is still far more frequent among mankind than is generally supposed. The white administrator through his ignorance is perhaps only hastening a movement towards individualism which was already in progress before his advent. Sometimes even he may be doing the right thing, but as in the case of chieftainship, it is not what he does but his way of doing it which is so especially harmful. People who see their institutions being upset by men whom they know to be acting in ignorance lose heart. They do not languish and die because their institutions are changed. They would perhaps welcome a change if its necessity were pointed out to them with considerateness and knowledge. The distrust bred of the ignorance of their rulers leads to the lack of interest in life which among such people is only the forerunner of extinction.

This essay has so far considered the value of anthropology to the government of subject peoples in relation to the task of that science in the collection and description of social facts. The other two tasks of the science can be considered very briefly.

It is not necessary to dwell upon the value to a ruler of a knowledge of the psychology of the people he is called upon to govern. The difficulty here is not so much to obtain recognition of this value as in the backward state of our knowledge. It is largely through our knowledge of custom and institution that we can expect to understand the psychology of savage and barbarous peoples[1]. Every advance in this direction will bring with it an advance towards the appreciation of the mental similarities and differences which are so important in the art of government.

Of the third task of anthropology, the inquiry into the history of social institutions and the laws which govern their growth and their decay, little need be said. The science is still only feeling its way towards the principles and methods by which these subjects may be studied, and any results so far reached can be of little practical importance. It is generally acknowledged, however, that a knowledge of the history of an institution is useful to the legislator or administrator who wishes to remove abuses, remedy defects, or devise measures which will adapt the institution to new conditions. We can be sure that, if this is true of civilised communities, it must also be true of the uncivilised. May we hope that, before the savage and barbarous peoples of the earth have become extinct or have become subject to the drab monotony which will result from too faithful an imitation of European

[1] *Sociological Review*, 1916, vol. ix, p. 1.

civilisation, we may have reached a knowledge of their history which will enable our rulers to take that broad view of their responsibilities towards the future which is so greatly assisted by a knowledge of the past?

Having now considered certain ways in which the science of anthropology can contribute to the better government of subject peoples, I can pass to the means by which this end may be attained. Two chief lines of action suggest themselves. One is the investigation of customs and beliefs by officers especially appointed for the task who give their whole time and energy to this employment. The other line of action is to give a knowledge of anthropology and its methods to those who are themselves to carry on the work of government. This may be done either before they enter on their work or in periods of study-leave especially granted for this purpose, or better still, by a combination of both courses. The first line of action may take two directions. Governments may appoint special officers, government anthropologists or ethnologists, to give their whole time to scientific inquiry, a plan adopted by the Government of Nigeria, or they may undertake ethnographic surveys such as have been carried out in recent years by the Governments of India and of the Anglo-Egyptian Sudan. The steps already taken in the latter direction have given valuable results and much is to be hoped from their continuance and extension.

Whichever direction is taken, however, this line of action would hardly touch the chief need. The knowledge acquired by special officers or by official surveys will only be second-hand to those upon whom falls the actual work of government. It can never have the interest or the practical value of knowledge acquired during the performance of their duties by officials trained to appreciate both the scientific and practical bearings of the facts which come before them. The knowledge accumulated by the work of specialists would be invaluable to officials who have been trained in anthropology or have themselves made anthropological inquiries, but it is of relatively little importance compared with the first-hand experience gained by men prepared for the work of government by being taught, or by having learnt for themselves, something of the vast variety of forms taken by the social conduct of mankind.

I propose now to consider very briefly the kind of education best adapted to the ends I have considered in the preceding pages. In any plan of education designed to fit the future rulers of a subject people for the performance of their duties it is essential that its ideal should not be that, far too frequent among us, in which education consists in the transmission of facts from the teacher to the taught. The knowledge needed is of the principles which underlie the vast variety of social institution and belief of mankind and of the methods by which

# THE EDUCATION NEEDED

this variety can be recorded, studied and reduced to order. A scheme of education the scope of which is limited to the special part of the earth in the ruling of which the student expects to take part would miss the point entirely. What is needed is the breadth of view which comes from a wide survey of human custom and belief, though this survey may well be supplemented by the more intensive study of some one part of the world. Whether the part of the world so studied is or is not that in which the student expects to live is a matter of no great importance. There are reasons why it would be more profitable to study intensively a region different from that in which the student expects to work.

Especially futile would be a system in which the instruction of the future rulers of any part of the world is undertaken by those who have already assisted in its government. Such a course of action would only perpetuate the bodies of false knowledge which have so frequently come into being (see p. 307), especially in the more recent acquisitions of the Empire. We need men who will go to the work of government with minds committed to no special point of view, but with an interest in the manifold problems which are being formulated by students of human society. Above all is it necessary that they shall realise how little we know and how much there is to learn.

It may, it almost certainly will, be objected that

the production of such a mental attitude on the part of those who have to carry out the practical work of government may lead to weakness and indecision on the executive side of this government. It must be acknowledged that there is this danger, and if the result of education in anthropology were to produce a doctrinaire and academical atmosphere among the rulers of our Empire there would be no one more ready to condemn it than the writer of this essay.

Such an objection, however, would be due to a failure to realise the mechanism by which the knowledge of native modes of thought and behaviour would be utilised for the promotion of better government. The formulation of lines of policy based upon knowledge would not be the work of executive officers but of the legislative side of the activities of governors and heads of departments. In order that such lines of policy may be framed it is necessary to know the facts, and it is the collection of these facts which would be the duty of the executive officers who come into direct contact with the people. It is just because the collection of these facts, if they are to be facts and not fancies, is no easy matter and demands special equipment and knowledge, that education in anthropology is so strongly advocated in this essay. There is nothing in the collection of facts which should interfere in any way with executive efficiency, and if, as may sometimes happen, junior executive officers are able

## DIFFICULTIES

to generalise and suggest to their superiors lines of action based upon the facts they have learnt, there should again be nothing to interfere in any way with practical efficiency.

It is when those who have collected facts and given some time and thought to their consideration come to occupy the higher positions in government that the policy advocated in this essay would bear its full fruits. Only those who have themselves studied facts at first-hand can properly appreciate those facts and especially their practical bearings. It is when those who direct the lines of policy to be adopted in the government of subject peoples have themselves a practical first-hand knowledge of the facts that we may look forward to the formulation of policies which will reconcile the general needs of the Empire with a due regard for the moral and material welfare of the peoples towards whom the Empire has so great a responsibility.

I have just considered and attempted to answer one objection which will be brought against the proposals of this essay, and I may take this opportunity to consider another. It will be urged that those who govern the subject peoples of the Empire have already as much to do as they can manage, and that it is impracticable to add to their already manifold duties that of collecting ethnographical facts.

To this objection there are two answers. First,

the facts which we need are mostly such as come before officials in the daily performance of their duties. The question is whether these facts shall be understood or misunderstood, and whether, if correctly noted and understood, the knowledge so acquired shall be limited to the official who has grasped their meaning or shall be put on record and utilised for the benefit of his colleagues and successors. At present too often in our colonies, the experience gained by a successful official disappears when he dies or leaves a colony and is of no use to his successors. To give a concrete instance: in the courts of any colony of the Empire cases are tried daily the settlement of which involves the collection of native evidence, and the eliciting of native ideas and modes of social conduct. Though such cases have rarely been published, they have afforded material of the utmost value to students of sociology. In our own country the whole structure of jurisprudence rests upon the record of cases. Such a record of cases and precedents will have to be built up sooner or later by similar collections in each of the countries governed by the Empire. If a beginning were made in this direction there would be begun a record by which the experience of existing officers would not only become available for the instruction of their colleagues and successors, but would also serve as most valuable material for students of the subject at home, by whose efforts towards the better understanding of the minds and actions of mankind the work of government would be assisted.

The objection I am considering, however, only forms part of a general attitude towards the whole question of the practical value of science. I do not suppose that there is a single proposal for the utilisation of science to which this kind of objection does not apply. Doing work properly must always at first demand a larger amount of time and trouble; the increased time and trouble in the first instance, however, will pay in the long run. There is no question whatever that many of our costly wars with subject peoples have been the direct consequence of ignorance. The question whether we should spend time and money now in order to prevent the wasteful expenditure of a much larger amount of time and money in the future only forms part of the more general question whether we are going to continue to govern our Empire on the lines of opportunism and "muddling through," or are going to face the situation and recognise that the time for such policies is past.

The British Empire has been built up by character rather than by intelligence. The great success of this mode of growth in the past should not blind us to its insufficiency for the future. The policy now advocated is not that character shall be replaced by intelligence, but that intelligence shall not be neglected, even despised, in the future as it has been in the past. The qualities needed to build up an Empire are not necessarily the same as those by which it will be maintained. We can only hope to stand against our competitors if we supplement the character which has been given to us by a larger exercise of the intelligence by which that gift has been accompanied. Science, the application of which to the work of government this essay advocates, is only our name for the product which results from the use of this intelligence.

Q
171
S5
1967

JAN 4 1972